A Direct Instruction Series

READING MASTERY

WORKBOOK IIIB

Siegfried Engelmann
Susan Hanner

Printed in the United States of America.

ISBN 0-574-08009-0

SRA ®

SCIENCE RESEARCH ASSOCIATES, INC.
Chicago, Palo Alto, Toronto
Henley-on-Thames, Sydney

A Subsidiary of IBM

LESSON 71

A

Story items

1. What did Linda and Kathy use for the blades of the water wheel?

_____

2. What did they use for the shaft? _____

3. What did they use for hammers? _____

4. a. How much did Linda weigh? _____

    b. How much did Kathy weigh? _____

    c. How much did the water wheel weigh? _____

5. Why was it so hard for the girls to move the water wheel? _____

_____

6. The picture below shows a stream in a streambed.
    a. Where would it be easier to walk, at **X** or at **Y**? _____

    b. Tell why. _____

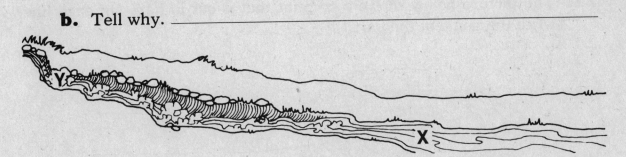

7. How high was the waterfall that the girls found? _____

Skill items

8. Compare a flat rock and a hammer. Remember what you're going to tell first and what you're going to tell next.

_____

_____

_____

Review items

9. **a.** How many shells do coconuts have? _____

   b. Is it easy to break open a coconut? _____

   c. Tell why. _____

   d. What is the juice inside a coconut called? _____

10. The picture below shows a coconut tree. On each line, write the name of the part.

   a. _____

   b. _____

   c. _____

   d. _____

11. The picture below shows a coconut that is cut in half. On each line, write the name of the part.

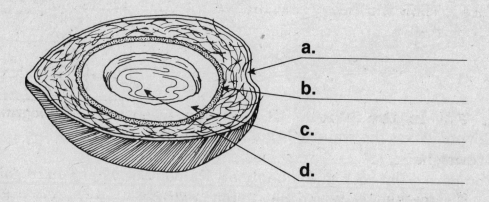

   a. _____

   b. _____

   c. _____

   d. _____

12. Look at the picture.
   a. Write **north, south, east,** and **west** in the right boxes.
   b. Write **noon** on the sun you see at noon.
   c. Write **early morning** on the sun you see early in the morning.
   d. Write **evening** on the sun you see in the evening.

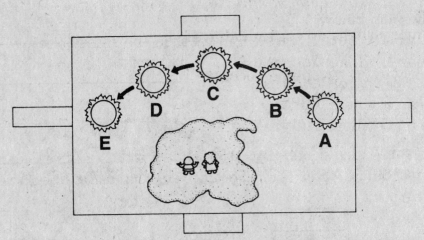

13. Look at the picture. It tells how many degrees each object is.

a. Which object is the hottest? _____

b. What is the temperature of that object? _____

c. Which object is the coldest? _____

d. What is the temperature of that object? _____

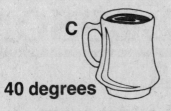

A   B   C

50 degrees   **30 degrees**   **40 degrees**

14. The dotted arrow shows which way the boy will jump. Make a solid arrow on the block of ice to show which way it will move.

15. a. Fill in the blanks. If something weighs one kilogram, it

weighs _____ grams.

b. If something weighs 8 kilograms, it weighs _____ grams.

16. a. Finish the sentence. Palm trees cannot live in places that get

_____

b. Name two things that grow on different palm trees.

① _____   ② _____

17. Look at the map below.
  a. Write **north, south, east,** and **west** in the right boxes.
  b. Make an **L** where **Japan** is.
  c. Make a **Z** where **China** is.
  d. Make an **F** where **Turkey** is.
  e. Make an **O** where **Italy** is.

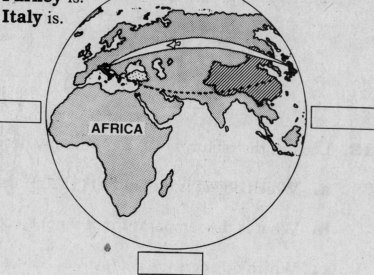

AFRICA

LESSON 72

ERRORS	WA	G	WB	BONUS	T

A

In today's lesson you read about liters. Use what you learned to do this these items.

  1. Look at the picture.
    a. **Circle** the containers in the picture that hold one liter.
    b. **Cross out** the containers that hold four liters.

  2. How much does a liter of fresh water weigh? _____

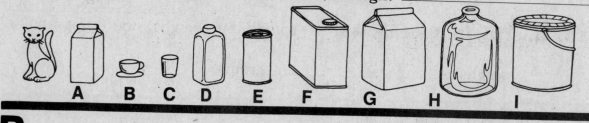

A   B   C   D   E   F   G   H   I

B

Story items
  3. **Finish the sentence.** The waterfall that Linda and Kathy found

  was dropping _____20_____ liters of water every second.

4. Waterfall A is dropping 8 liters of water every second. Waterfall B is dropping 40 liters of water every second. Which waterfall has more force? _Waterfall B_

5. a. What did Linda and Kathy make to hold back the stream?

They used rocks to huld back the stream

b. What did they make it out of? _a logs nales and bords_

6. The picture below shows the water wheel under the waterfall.
  a. Draw an arrow to show which way A will move.
  b. Start at B and draw an arrow around the shaft to show which way it will turn.
  c. Draw an arrow at C to show which way the vine will move when the shaft turns.

7. What did the girls use to support the shaft of the water wheel?

_____

8. What did Linda use to grease the ends of the shaft? _____

9. Kathy thought it was a long way from the water wheel to the beach.

  Tell why. _____

10. How was Kathy going to signal when the net was full of fish?

_____

11. Compare Linda and Kathy. Remember what you're going to tell first and what you're going to tell next.

_____

_____

_____

Review items

12. a. Finish the sentence. If something weighs one kilogram, it

weighs _____ grams.

   b. Finish the sentence. If something weighs seven kilograms, it

weighs _____ grams.

13. The picture below shows a stream in a streambed.

   a. Where would it be easier to walk, at A or at B? _____

   b. Tell why. _____

14. a. Finish the sentence. Palm trees cannot live in places that get

_____.

   b. What are the branches of palm trees called? _____

   c. Name two things that grow on different palm trees.

     ① _____ ② _____

15. Look at the map.

   a. What part of the world is shown on the map? _____

   b. The map shows how far apart some cities are. Some cities are two thousand kilometers apart and some cities are four thousand kilometers apart.

     • Write **2** in the box if the line stands for two thousand kilometers.

     • Write **4** in the box if the line stands for four thousand kilometers.

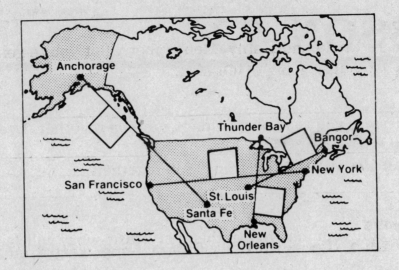

16. Look at the picture below.

   a. Which turtle is going faster? _____

   b. How fast is that turtle going? _____

   c. Which car is going faster? _____

   d. How fast is that car going? _____

   e. Which truck is going faster? _____

   f. How fast is that truck going? _____

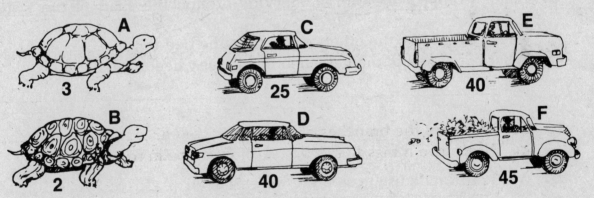

17. Look at the columns of words below.

   a. Cross out all the words in the **eat** family.

   b. Make a box around all the words in the **sit** family.

running	ate	sitting	flew
eaten	sat	ran	eating
jumped	race	eats	jumper
sits	eat	writer	talked
talk	flying	sitter	sit

LESSON 73

A

In today's lesson, you read about things rubbing together. Use what you learned to do these items.

1. **Finish the rule.** When things rub together, _____

   _____

2. If you rub your hands together very fast, what will happen to your

   hands? _____

3. If you rub two pencils together very fast, what will happen to the

   pencils? _____

B

Story items

4. How did Kathy signal Linda when the net was full of fish?

   _____

5. Linda wrapped one end of the vine around the shaft of the water

   wheel. What was the other end of the vine tied to? _____

6. What happened to the net when the water wheel turned?

   _____

7. What was in the net? _____

8. What did Linda use to stop the water wheel? _____

9. Did the girls eat all the fish that were in the net? _____

10. **a.** Linda pounded a nail into one end of the trunk. What did she

    press against the nail as it turned? _____

    b. And what happened to the nail when it rubbed against the rock?

    _____

    c. What started to burn when the nail got hot? _____

11. The picture shows the water wheel under the waterfall.
   a. Draw an arrow to A to show which way A will move.
   b. Start at B and draw an arrow around the shaft to show which way it will turn.
   c. Draw an arrow at C to show which way the vine will move when the shaft turns.

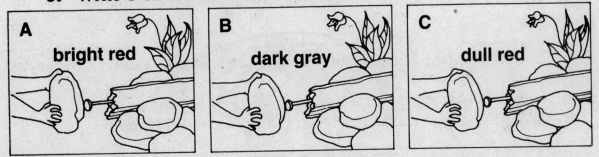

12. The words next to each nail tell the color of that nail. Figure out how hot each nail is.
   a. Write **1** on the nail that is hottest.
   b. Write **2** on the nail that is next-hottest.
   c. Write **3** on the nail that is coldest.

A	B	C
bright red	**dark gray**	**dull red**

Review items
13. Waterfall X is dropping 60 liters of water every second. Waterfall Y is dropping 80 liters of water every second. Which waterfall has more force? _____

14. a. Circle the containers in the picture that hold one liter.
   b. Underline the containers that hold four liters.

A B C D E F G H I

15. Look at the picture below.
 a. Write **north, south, east,** and **west** in the right boxes.
 b. An arrow goes from the R. Which direction is that arrow going?

_____

 c. Make an arrow that
  goes **east** from the Q.
 d. Draw the smoke in the picture.

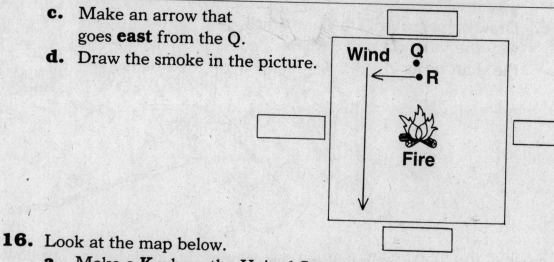

16. Look at the map below.
 a. Make a **K** where the United States is.
 b. Make a **T** where Canada is.
 c. Make an **L** where Mexico is.
 d. Make an **R** where South America is.

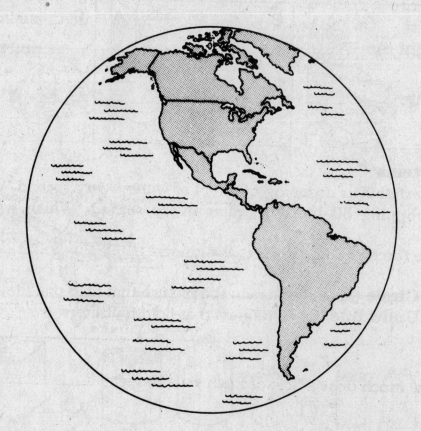

17. The dotted arrow shows which way the bullet will leave the gun. Make a solid arrow on the gun to show which way it will move.

18. Look at the map below.
   a. What part of the world is shown on the map? _____
   b. The map shows how far apart some cities are. Some cities are two thousand kilometers apart and some cities are four thousand kilometers apart.
   • Write **2** in the box if the line stands for two thousand kilometers.
   • Write **4** in the box if the line stands for four thousand kilometers.

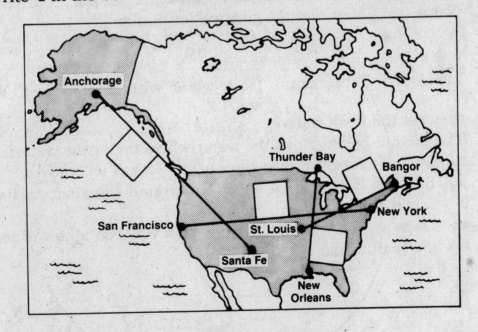

19. How much does a liter of fresh water weigh? _____

LESSON 74

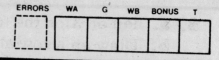

A

Story items

1. Linda and Kathy made a fire by rubbing two objects together. Name those two objects. ① _____ ② _____

2. Why did the girls move the fire to the beach? _____ _____

3. **a.** What did Kathy have to do to the outside of the fish?

   _____

   b. What did she use for a tool? _____

4. **a.** What was Linda's job when the girls cleaned the fish?

   _____

   b. What did she use for a tool? _____

   c. How did she make her tool sharp? _____

5. Name two things that the girls ate for dinner.

   ① _____ ② _____

6. Linda and Kathy drank fresh water with their dinner. Where did they get the fresh water? _____

7. The picture below shows the water wheel under the waterfall.
   a. Draw an arrow at A to show which way A will move.
   b. Start at B and draw an arrow around the shaft to show which way it will turn.
   c. Draw an arrow at C to show which way the vine will move when the shaft turns.

8. a. Put an **X** on the tool that Kathy used to scale the fish.

  b. Draw an arrow above the tool to show which direction the tool is moving.

Review items

  9. a. Finish the rule. When things rub together, _____

  _____

  b. If you rub two sticks together very fast, what will happen to the

  sticks? _____

  c. If you rub your hands together very fast, what will happen to

  your hands? _____

10. Look at the map below.

  a. Make a **U** where the United States is.

  b. Make a **D** where Canada is.

  c. Make a **T** where South America is.

  d. Make an **A** where Mexico is.

11. Look at the picture.
   a. Write **north, south, east,** and **west** in the right boxes.
   b. An arrow goes from the M. Which direction is that arrow going?

_____

   c. Make an arrow that goes **north**
      from the P.
   d. Draw the smoke in the picture.

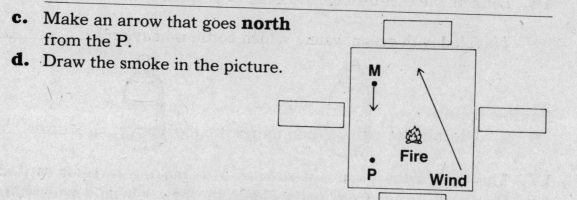

12. Make an **I** on each island
   in the picture.

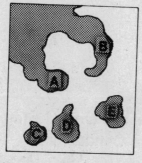

13. The words next to each nail tell the color of that nail. Figure out how
   hot each nail is.
   a. Write **1** on the nail that is hottest.
   b. Write **2** on the nail that is next-hottest.
   c. Write **3** on the nail that is coldest.

14. The picture below shows jars of water on a very cold day.
   a. What is the temperature of the water in each jar? _____
   b. Write an **X** on each jar that is filled with ocean water.
   c. Jar F is not filled with ocean water. How do you know? _____

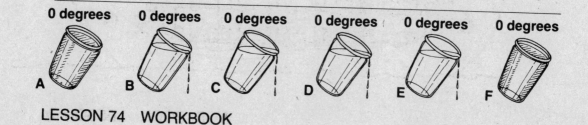

15. a. What does ocean water taste like? _____

b. What will happen if you drink lots of ocean water?

_____

16. Look at the picture below. Bottle D is filled with fresh water. Bottle

J is filled with ocean water. Which bottle is heavier? _____

D   J

17. The ship in the picture is sinking. It is making currents as it sinks. Make an arrow from each object to show which way it is being pulled.

18. Look at the picture of an ocean liner.
a. Put an **X** on two bulkheads.
b. Put a **C** on two decks.
c. Put a **K** at the prow.
d. Put an **O** at the stern.

LESSON 75

A

In today's lesson, you read about fevers. Use what you learned to do these items.

1. What is the temperature inside your body when you are healthy?

_____

2. Fill in the blank. Most fevers don't go over _____ degrees.

3. Name two things that may happen when people have very high

fevers. ① _____

② _____

B

Story items

4. How long had Linda and Kathy been on the island when they saw

the airplane? _____

5. Did the people in the plane see Linda and Kathy? _____

6. What did the girls use to make a signal for planes? _____

7. a. What word did they spell? _____

b. Fill in the blank. The word was over _____ meters long.

8. What kind of signal did the girls make for ships? _____

9. Why did the fire smoke so much? _____

_____

10. How did Linda know that Kathy had a fever? _____

11. Finish the sentence. Linda thought that Kathy's temperature was

over _____

12. Did Linda think that Kathy was really seeing a ship? _____

Review items

13. a. How many legs does an insect have? _____

b. How many legs does a fly have? _____

c. How many legs does a flea have? _____

d. How many legs does a water strider have? _____

e. How many legs does an ant have? _____

f. How many legs does a spider have? _____

14. Some lines in the box below are one centimeter long. **Circle** the lines that are one centimeter long.

15. a. Name a state in the United States that is bigger than Italy. _____

b. Finish the sentence. Italy is shaped something like a _____

16. Underline the plane in the picture that is in the coldest air.

5 kilometers high

4 kilometers high

3 kilometers high

2 kilometers high

1 kilometer high

17. Look at the picture of an ocean liner.
  a. Put a **B** on two bulkheads.
  b. Put a **V** on two decks.
  c. Put an **L** at the prow.
  d. Put a **W** at the stern.

18. Look at the map below.
  a. Write **east** next to the city on the east coast.
  b. Write **west** next to the city on the west coast.
  c. Draw an arrow to show the trip from New York City to San Francisco.
  d. Make an **F** where Denver is.
  e. Make an **M** where Chicago is.
  f. Make a **P** where Salt Lake City is.

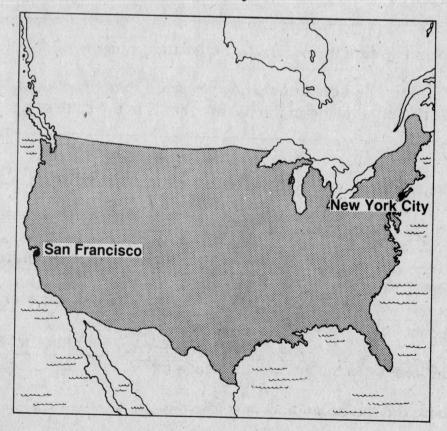

San Francisco

New York City

LESSON 76

A

In today's lesson you learned about landing a ship. Use what you learned to do this item.

1. Look at the picture.
   a. Put a **T** on the tugboat.
   b. Put a **D** on two docks.
   c. Put an **S** on two ships.

B

Story items

2. What kind of signal did Linda and Kathy use so the people on the ship would see them? _____

3. Why did the fire smoke so much? _____

_____

4. What was the name of the ship that rescued the girls? _____

5. Why was Kathy's forehead hot? _____

6. Linda showed Captain Reeves things that she and Kathy had used to survive on the island. Some of those things are listed below. **Underline** those things.
   - water wheel
   - knife
   - books
   - house
   - signal for airplanes

7. How long were the girls on the ocean liner? _____

8. Where did the ocean liner take them? _____

9. Who was in the crowd that gathered to meet the ship? _____

_____

Review items

10. a. What is the temperature inside your body when you are

healthy? _____

b. Fill in the blank. Most fevers don't go over _____ degrees.

c. Name two things that may happen when people have very high

fevers. ① _____

② _____

11. Look at the map below.

   a. Write **east** next to the city on the east coast.

   b. Write **west** next to the city on the west coast.

   c. Draw an arrow to show the trip from New York City to San Francisco.

   d. Make an **F** where Denver is.

   e. Make a **B** where Chicago is.

   f. Make a **J** where Salt Lake City is.

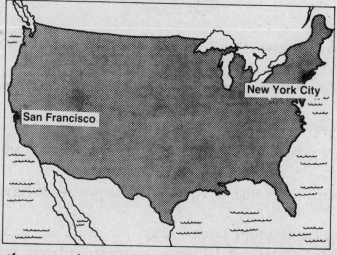

12. a. **Circle** the containers in the picture that hold one liter.

   b. **Cross out** the containers that hold four liters.

A   B   C   D E F   G   H   I

13. Look at the lines in the box below.
  a. Write **1** on each line that is 1 centimeter long.
  b. Write **3** on each line that is 3 centimeters long.

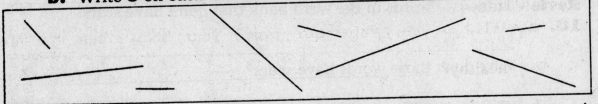

14. a. Fill in the blanks. If something weighs one kilogram, it

weighs _____ grams.
  b. If something weighs six kilograms, it weighs _____ grams.

  c. How much does a liter of fresh water weigh? _____

15. The picture below shows a coconut that is cut in half. On each line, write the name of the part.

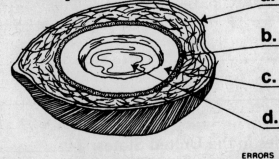

a. _____

b. _____

c. _____

d. _____

ERRORS	WA	G	WB	BONUS	T

LESSON 77

A

In today's lesson, you read about mosquitoes. Use what you learned to do these items.

  1. If a mosquito is an insect, how many legs does it have? _____

  2. Where are mosquitoes born? _____

  3. Finish the sentence. When a mosquito is born, it is called a

  _____

  4. What do mosquitoes have to do before they can lay eggs?

  _____

Story items

  5. Is Hohoboho a real place or is it a make-believe place?

  _____

6. How did some words in the word bank get scars?

_____

7. a. Name two words in the word bank that don't have scars.

① _____ ② _____

b. Why don't those words have scars?

_____

8. Each word in the columns fought with a word in the box. Next to each word in the columns, write the word it was fighting with. Be sure to spell each word correctly.

go	run	their	to	from	write	had
saw	hear	eight	you	for	nine	

a. right _____ **d.** two _____

b. here _____ **e.** ate _____

c. there _____ **f.** four _____

Review items

9. Name four cities in the United States. ① _____

② _____ ③ _____ ④ _____

10. Name three relatives of the word **run.**

① _____ ② _____ ③ _____

11. Look at the picture below.

a. Make an arrow **over** each canoe to show which way the canoe is moving.

b. Make an arrow **under** each paddle to show which way the paddle is moving in the water.

12. Look at the picture.
   a. Put a **J** on the tugboat.
   b. Put a **P** on two docks.
   c. Put an **O** on two ships.

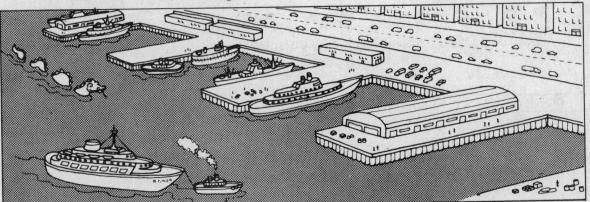

13. Waterfall J is dropping 12 liters of water every second. Waterfall P is dropping 8 liters of water every second. Which waterfall has more

force? _____

14. Look at the map below.
   a. Write **north, south, east,** and **west** in the right places.
   b. Make a **T** where Japan is.
   c. Make a **U** where China is.
   d. Make a **B** where Turkey is.
   e. Make an **L** where
   Italy is.

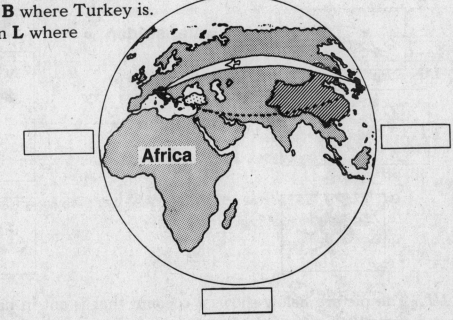

15. Figure out this animal. It is born in the water, and it lives in the water until it is full grown. Then it moves onto the land. It has smooth skin and a long tongue. Its back legs are big and strong.

What is it? _____

16. a. Make an **I** in front of the name of every insect.
  b. Draw a line from each name to the right animal.

fly •

poodle •

mole •

pointer •

flea •

beagle •

frog •

toad •

reindeer •

water strider •

tadpole •

mosquito •

spider •

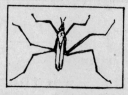

17. The picture below shows a coconut that is cut in half. On each line, write the name of the part.

a. _____

b. _____

c. _____

d. _____

LESSON 78

A

Story items

1. The words **there** and **their** were always fighting because they are the same in one way. Name that way.

   _____

2. The word **three** did not have fights. Why not? _____

   _____

3. The word **one** had fights with another word. Write that word. Be

   sure to spell that word correctly. _____

4. The word **four** had fights with another word. Write that word. Be

   sure to spell that word correctly. _____

5. The word **eight** had fights with another word. Write that word. Be

   sure to spell that word correctly. _____

6. Which word in the word bank had the most scars? _____

7. Write two words that the word **two** had fights with. Spell the words

   correctly. ① _____   ② _____

Skill items

8. Compare the word **two** and the word **to**. Remember what you're going to tell first and what you're going to tell next.

   _____

   _____

   _____

Review items

9. **Figure out this animal.** It is about one meter tall at the shoulder. It lives in places that are very cold. It is used to pull sleds and to give

   milk. It has antlers. What is it? _____

10. Name five animals that are warm-blooded. ① _____

② _____ ③ _____

④ _____ ⑤ _____

11. The picture below shows a stream in a streambed.

   a. Where would it be easier to walk, at L or at T? _____

   b. Tell why. _____

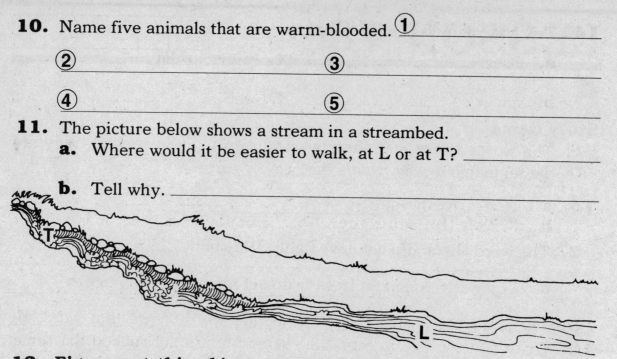

12. Figure out this object. You can look through it. When you look

through it, things look very, very big. What is it? _____

13. You know the names of the countries that are marked on the following maps. Next to each letter, write the name of the country that the arrow points to.

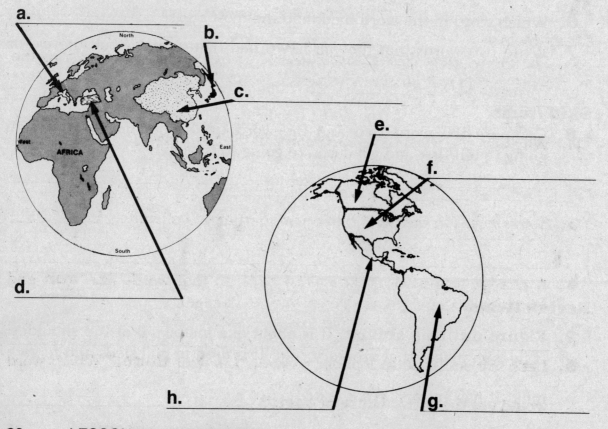

14. Tell how many legs each thing has.

a. insect _____   **e.** water strider _____

b. spider _____   **f.** ant _____

c. fly _____   **g.** mosquito _____

d. flea _____

15. a. Where are mosquitoes born? _____
   b. Finish the sentence. When a mosquito is born, it is called a

   _____

   c. What do mosquitoes have to do before they can lay eggs?

   _____

16. Write two words that sound the same but are not spelled the same. Be sure to spell the words correctly.

①_____   ②_____

LESSON 79

ERRORS	WA	G	WB	BONUS	T

A

Story items

1. The words **new** and **knew** had lots of fights because they are the same in one way. Name that way.

_____

2. Why was the word bank calm early in the morning?

_____

3. Some words in the word bank wore earplugs. Tell why. _____

_____

4. A change was made in the word bank so that words like **won** and **one** would stop fighting. What was the change?

_____

5. Let's say someone in Hohoboho said, "It's over **there**." Which word would get the point, **there** or **their**? _____

6. Let's say someone in Hohoboho said, "I have **two** dogs." Which word would get the point, **to, too,** or **two?** _____

7. Were there any more fights in the word bank after the change was made? _____

Skill items

8. Compare the word **eight** and the word **ate.** Remember what you're going to tell first and what you're going to tell next.

_____

_____

_____

9. Fill in the blanks.

Henry Ouch went for a vacation. He left San Francisco on a large ship. That ship went to Japan. Which direction did the ship go? _____

How far was that trip? _____

What ocean did Henry cross? _____
The ship passed some islands. How did Henry know they were islands? _____
Henry could see palm trees on some islands. He knew that the branches of a palm tree are called _____. He also knew the name of the large hard things that grow on some palm trees. What are those things called? _____ When Henry got thirsty, he drank little drops of water that formed on the deck early in the morning. What are those drops called? _____

Henry did not drink water from the ocean. Why not? _____

_____

Henry was very strong, but he could not carry a liter of fresh water. How much does a liter of fresh water weigh? _____

Henry did not like it when the temperature dropped because Henry's body worked like the bodies of other insects. Henry was

_____-blooded. Sometimes the temperature inside his body was higher than your normal temperature. What's your normal

body temperature? _____

Sometimes the temperature inside his body was lower than your normal temperature. When would the temperature inside his body

get lower? _____

10. **a. Fill in the blank.** Most fevers don't go over _____ degrees.
 b. Name two things that may happen when people have very high

   fevers.① _____

   ② _____

11. **Figure out what is being described.** It is made to carry passengers. It can move over 8 hundred kilometers per hour. A pilot

and flight attendants work on it. _____

12. Here's a picture of a jet.
 a. Draw a dotted arrow from a jet engine to show which way the air will move.
 b. Draw a solid arrow on the plane to show which way it will move.

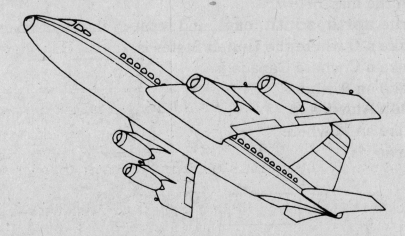

13. Name a state in the United States that is bigger than Japan. _____

14. **Figure out this animal.** It is born in the water and it lives in the water until it is full grown. Then it moves onto the land. Its skin is

rough and covered with warts. What is it? _____

15. **a.** Write **WB** in front of the name of every warm-blooded animal.
   b. Draw a line from each name to the right animal.

reindeer •

fly •

beagle •

flea •

poodle •

water strider •

spider •

pointer •

16. Look at the map below.
   a. Write **north, south, east,** and **west** in the right boxes.
   b. Make a **U** where the United States is.
   c. Make a **C** where Canada is.
   d. Make an **A** where South America is.
   e. Make an **M** where Mexico is.

LESSON 80

ERRORS	WA	G	CO	WB	BONUS	T

A

Story items

1. New fights started as soon as the words were written on the screen.
   a. The words that fought were the same in one way. Name that
   way. _They were spelld the same._
   b. How were they different from each other?
   They were seed diffrit

2. Some words from the word bank are in List 1. Some words in List 2 sound the same as words in List 1. Here's the rule: If a word in List 2 sounds the same as a word in List 1, draw a line between the words. One item is done for you.

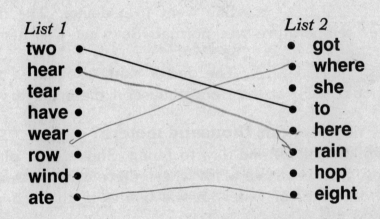

List 1
- two
- hear
- tear
- have
- wear
- row
- wind
- ate

List 2
- got
- where
- she
- to
- here
- rain
- hop
- eight

3. Let's say that someone in Hohoboho said "Those dogs had a terrible **row." Finish the sentence.** The word that would get the point

   rhymes with _how_ • how • no
4. Let's say that someone in Hohoboho said, "Do you **live** here?" **Finish the sentence.** The word that would get the point rhymes

   with _give_ • dive • give
5. Someone in Hohoboho said, "Did you **read** this book?" **Finish the**

   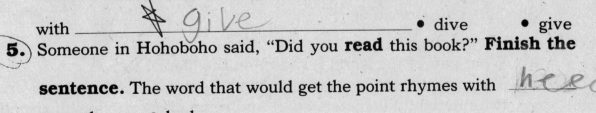

   sentence. The word that would get the point rhymes with _need_

   • need   • bed

Review items

6. Fill in the blanks.

A jet pilot went around the world. She went from the country of

Japan to Italy. In what direction was she going? _____

Then she continued in the same direction until she came to a
country that is much larger than Japan or Italy. What's the name of

that large country? _____ She landed
her jet plane in a city on the east coast of the country. Name a city

on the east coast of that country. _____

When the wheels of the plane touched the runway, they rubbed
against the runway and you know what happened to the temperature

of the wheels. What happened to the temperature? _____

The pilot was not feeling well. She thought she had a slight fever.
What would her temperature be if she had a slight fever?

_____ She went to a doctor. The doctor told her
that her temperature was normal. So what was her temperature?

_____ The doctor said, "You need more exercise.
You should walk at least one thousand meters every day." What's

another name for **one thousand meters?** _____

The pilot took off and flew to Japan. She left her plane and took a
vacation. She went to a place where there was a water wheel. Every
second, one liter of water hit the blades of that wheel. How much

weight is that? _____ Around
the water were insects that were born in the water and sucked blood.

What kind of insects were those? _____

The pilot stayed away from those insects. Why did she stay away

from them? _____
She had a nice vacation.

7. Look at the map.
  a. What part of the world is shown on the map? _____
  b. The map shows how far apart some cities are. Some cities are
  two thousand kilometers apart and some cities are four thousand
  kilometers apart.

- Write **2** in the box if the line stands for two thousand kilometers.
- Write **4** in the box if the line stands for four thousand kilometers.

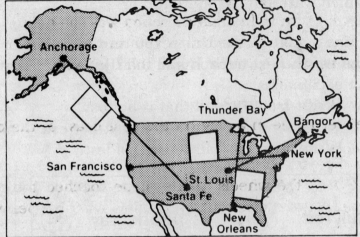

8. **Figure out what is being described.** It is made to carry passengers. It is a very large ship. It has a prow, a stern, decks, and bulkheads.

   What is it? _____

9. Name five insects. ① _____ ② _____

   ③ _____ ④ _____ ⑤ _____

10. Look at the map below.
    a. Write **east** next to the city on the east coast.
    b. Write **west** next to the city on the west coast.
    c. Draw an arrow to show the trip from New York City to San Francisco.
    d. Make a **Y** where Denver is.
    e. Make a **T** where Chicago is.
    f. Make an **L** where Salt Lake City is.

11. Waterfall A is dropping 2 hundred liters of water every second. Waterfall B is dropping 8 hundred liters of water every second.

Which waterfall has more force? _____

12. Name a state in the United States that is bigger than Italy. _____

13. The words next to each nail tell the color of that nail. Figure out how hot each nail is.
   a. Write **1** on the nail that is hottest.
   b. Write **2** on the nail that is next-hottest.
   c. Write **3** on the nail that is coldest.

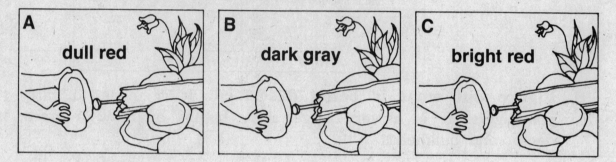

14. Look at the picture.
   a. Write **north, south, east,** and **west** in the right boxes.

   b. Which animal is facing into the wind? _____

   c. Which direction is that animal facing? _____

   d. So what's the name of the wind? _____

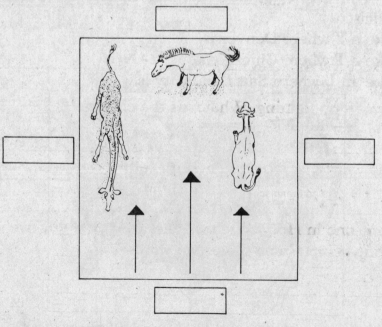

LESSON 81

A

In today's lesson, you read about contractions. Use what you learned to do these items.

1. For each contraction below, write the two words that make up the contraction.

CONTRACTION	FIRST WORD	SECOND WORD
a. you'll	you	will
b. I've	I	have
c. he'll	he	will
d. shouldn't	shouldn	not
e. we're	we	have
f. aren't	are	not

B

Story items

2. The words **one** and **won** used to fight because they are the same in one way. Name that way. _They sownd the same_

3. Write two words that the word **two** used to have fights with. Spell the words correctly. _to too_

4. A change was made in the word bank so that words like **one** and **won** would stop fighting. What was the change?
   They put it on the scren.

5. Write the word that would fight with **tear** if the words were written.
   Tear

6. **a.** If someone in Hohoboho said the word **you've**, two words would get one point. Name those two words.
   you you've

   b. Name the word that would get one-half point. _have_

7. **a.** If someone in Hohoboho said the word **wouldn't,** two words would get one point. Name those two words.

wouldn wouldnt

b. Name the word that would get one-half point. _nor_

8. Write the letters that are missing for each contraction.

a. couldn't _o_   **c.** she'll _wi_

b. we've _ha_   **d.** you're _a_

Review items

9. Look at the picture of the balloon.
 a. Make a dotted arrow to show which way the air will leave the balloon.
 b. Make a solid arrow on the balloon to show which way it will move.

10. Look at the map below.
 a. Make a **J** where Japan is.
 b. Make a **C** where China ia.
 c. Make a **T** where Turkey is.
 d. Make an **I** where Italy is.

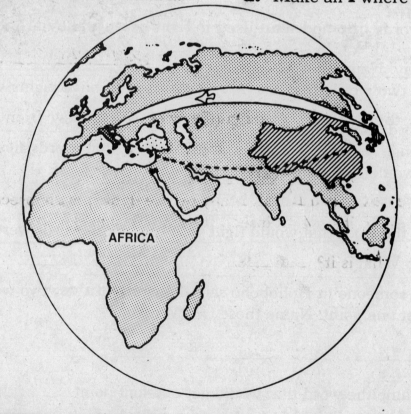

AFRICA

11. Write two words that sound the same but are not spelled the same. Be sure to spell the words correctly.

① _____ ② _____

12. Look at the map below.
  • Things that are this far apart on the map ←————→ are 3 kilometers apart.
  • Things that are this far apart ←————————→ are 6 kilometers apart.
  a. Write **3** in the circle if the line stands for 3 kilometers.
  b. Write **6** in the circle if the line stands for 6 kilometers.

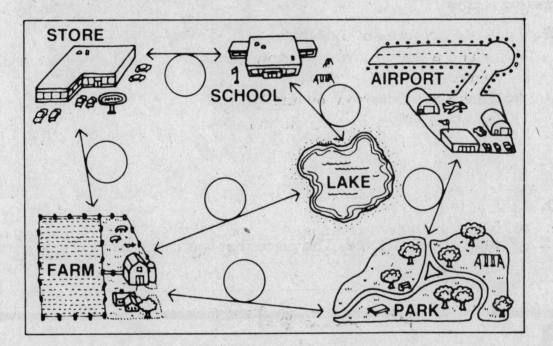

13. Name three cities you might fly over if you flew from New York City to San Francisco.

① _____ ② _____ ③ _____

14. Figure out this animal. Many people think it is an insect, but it has eight legs so it's not an insect. It usually makes a web to catch insects to eat. What is it? _____

LESSON 82

A

In today's lesson, you read about Troy and Greece. Use what you learned to do these items.

1. Look at the map.

a. Make a **K** where Troy used to be.

b. Make a **P** where Greece is.

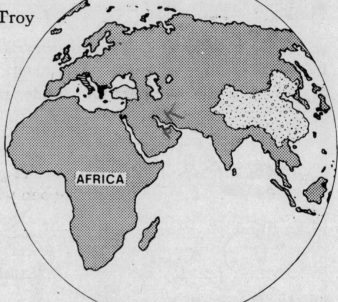

AFRICA

2. Finish the sentence. The place that was called Troy is now part of

the country of _____.

B

Story items

✱✱ **3.** What year is it now? _2008_

✱✱ **4.** What year were you born in? _1997_

✱ **5.** Around what year was the first airplane made? _1900_

✱ **6.** What was the year 1 hundred years ago? _1908_

✱ **7.** What was the year 2 hundred years ago? _1808_

✱ **8.** In what year did the United States become a country? _1776_

✱ **9.** What was the year 3 hundred years ago? _1708_

Review items

10. Write the letters that are missing for each contraction.

~~**a.**~~ you'll _____Wi_____   ~~**c.**~~ we've _____ha_____

~~**b.**~~ he'll _____Wi_____   **d.** ~~aren't~~ _____o_____

11. Let's say that someone in Hohoboho said, "Did you **tear** this page?"
Finish the sentence. The word that would get the point rhymes

with _____hair_____   • fear   • hair

STOP

12. a. What is the temperature inside your body when you are

healthy? _____97.8   98.4_____

b. **Fill in the blank.** Most fevers don't go over _____102_____ degrees.

c. Name two things that may happen when people have very high

fevers. ① _____they cuold dir o_____

② _____

13. Look at the picture below.
a. Make a **B** on the tugboat.
b. Make an **X** on two docks.   **c.** Make a **Y** on two ships.

14. a. **Cross out** the containers in the picture below that hold 1 liter.
b. **Circle** the containers that hold 4 liters.

A   B   C   D   E   F   G   H   I

15. The picture below shows a stream in a streambed.
    a. Where would it be easier to walk, at J or at K? _____

    b. Tell why. _____

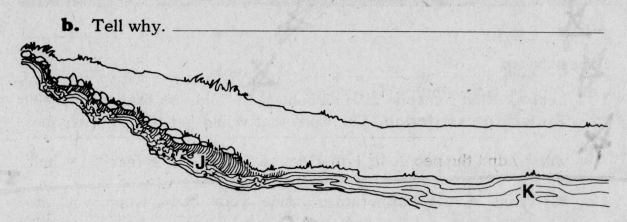

16. Waterfall B is dropping 60 liters of water every second. Waterfall L is dropping 40 liters of water every second. Which waterfall has

more force? _____

17. a. Finish the rule. When things rub together, _____

_____

    b. If you rub two rocks together very fast, what will happen to the

rocks? _____

18. Look at the picture below.
    a. Write **north, south, east,** and **west** in the right boxes.
    b. Write **noon** on the sun you see at noon.
    c. Write **early morning** on the sun you see early in the morning.
    d. Write **evening** on the sun you see in the evening.

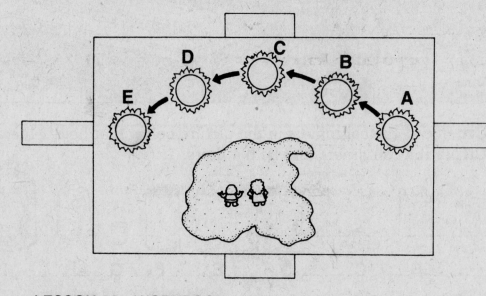

LESSON 83

A

Story items

1. When did the story of Troy take place?

3000 years ago

2. Why didn't the people in Troy have cars?

becas Henry Ford vaseht born
because   *wasn't*

3. How did the people of Troy get in and out of the city? a oart
                                                            gate

4. Name four weapons that soldiers used when they had battles with Troy.

① a shelb   *shield*

② a sord   *sword*

③ a shove   *shovel*

④ a lader   *ladder*

5. When an army put ladders against the wall of Troy, what did the people of Troy do? Pushed them over

6. When an army dug holes under the wall, what did the people of Troy do? boyling water

7. When an army tried to knock down the gate, what did the people of Troy do? throw arras at them

8. Why couldn't an army starve the people of Troy?

thay hade resorses
        resources.

9. Look at the map below.
   a. Write **north, south, east,** and **west** in the right boxes.
   b. Make a **T** where Troy used to be.
   c. Make an **R** where Greece is.

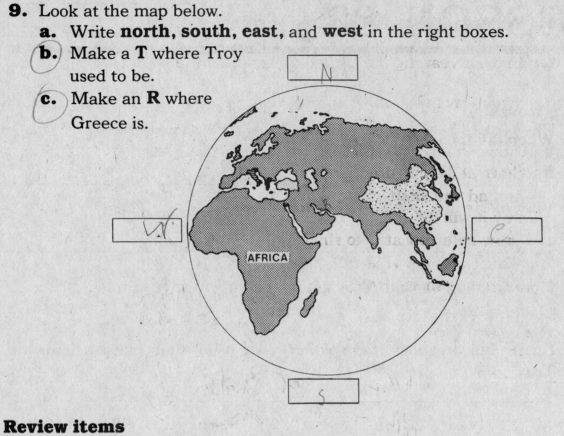

N

W

C

AFRICA

S

Review items

10. For each contraction below, write the two words that make up the contraction.

CONTRACTION	FIRST WORD	SECOND WORD
a. she'll	She	will
b. didn't	did	hot
c. I've	I	have
d. we're	we	are

11. Write two words that sound the same but are not spelled the same. Be sure to spell the words correctly. ① _____ ② _____

12. a. What year is it now? _____

   b. What year were you born in? _____

   c. Around what year was the first airplane made? _____

   d. What was the year 1 hundred years ago? _____

e. What was the year 2 hundred years ago? _____

f. In what year did the United States become a country? _____

g. What was the year 3 hundred years ago? _____

13. The picture below shows a water wheel under a waterfall.
   a. Draw an arrow to show which way A will move.
   b. Start at B and draw an arrow around the shaft to show which way it will move.
   c. Draw an arrow at C to show which way the vine will move when the shaft turns.

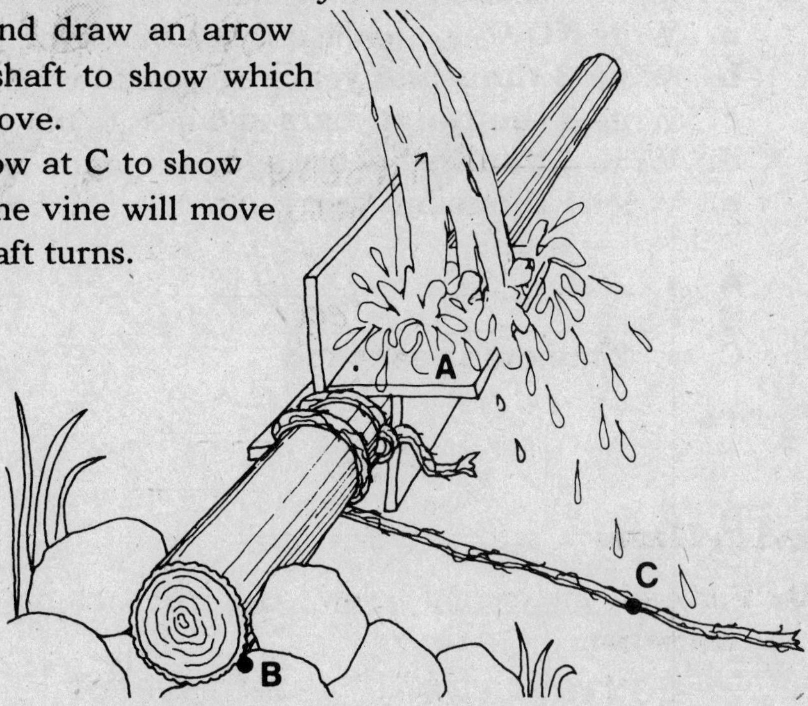

14. Tell how many legs each thing has.

   a. water strider _____   **e.** dog _____

   b. flea _____   **f.** insect _____

   c. spider _____   **g.** mosquito _____

   d. fly _____

15. a. Where are mosquitoes born? _____

   b. **Finish the sentence.** When a mosquito is born, it is called a

   _____

   c. What do mosquitoes have to do before they can lay eggs?

   _____

LESSON 84

ERRORS	WA	G	WB	BONUS	†

A

In today's lesson, you learned about a time line. Use what you learned to do these items.

1. Fill in the blanks on the time line.

- **a.** Write **NOW** next to the dot that shows the year now.
- **b.** Write **3 thousand years ago** next to the right dot.
- **c.** Write **2 thousand years ago** next to the right dot.
- **d.** Write **1 hundred years ago** next to the right dot.
- **e.** Write **1 thousand years ago** next to the right dot.

A • NOW

B • 1 hundred years ago

C • 2 hundred years ago

D • 1 thousall years ago

E • 2 thousand years ago

F • 3 thousand years ago

2. How long ago did the story of Troy take place?

3000 thousand years ago

3. About how long ago did Jesus Christ live?

200 thousand years ago

B

Story items

4. Why did Greece go to war with Troy? _because the queen_
would not go back to (Greece)

5. How many ships sailed to Troy? ___1000___

6. When the Greek army put ladders against the wall of Troy, what
did the people of Troy do? _pushed them down_

7. When the Greek army dug holes under the wall, what did the
people of Troy do? _pord boiling water down the hole_

8. When the Greek army tried to knock down the gate, what did the
people of Troy do? _They throw spears at them_

9. Why couldn't the Greek army starve the people of Troy?
they had resources

10. How long did the war go on? _10 years_

11. The Greek army wanted to get a few men inside the wall of Troy.
Tell why. _to open the gate_

Review items

12. Look at the map.
  a. Write **north, south, east,** and **west** in the right boxes.
  b. Draw an arrow on the cloud to show which way the cloud will
  move.
  c. What's the name of the wind
  that will move the cloud?

  _____

because
queen
would
down
pour
hole

spears
resources
open
gate

San Francisco

13. Write the letters that are missing for each contraction.

    a. you'll _____

    b. couldn't _____

    c. we've _____

    d. they're _____

14. a. What year were you born in? _____

    b. Around what year was the first airplane made? _____

    c. What was the year 1 hundred years ago? _____

    d. What was the year 2 hundred years ago? _____

    e. In what year did the United States become a country? _____

    f. What was the year 3 hundred years ago? _____

15. Why didn't the people in Troy have trucks? _____

_____

16. a. Fill in the blanks. If something weighs 1 kilogram, it weighs

_____ grams.

    b. If something weighs 10 kilograms, it weighs _____

    grams.

    c. How much does a liter of fresh water weigh? _____

LESSON 85

A

Story items

1. The army of Greece kept using the same four plans to get inside Troy. Name those four plans.

   ① *They would try to get over the wall*
   ② *they would try to dig under the wall*
   ③ *they would try to knock down the gate*
   ④ *they would starv them.*

2. How long did the war between Greece and Troy go on? *10 years*

3. What did the Greek army build to help them get inside Troy?

   They mayd a great woodenhorse

4. Where did the army put the horse after they finished building it?

   _____

5. What did the people of Troy think the wooden horse was?

   _____

6. After the people of Troy fell asleep, what came out of the horse?

   _____

7. What did they do after they came out of the horse?

   _____

8. Was the great wooden horse a gift, or was it a trick?

   _____

9. Who won the war — Troy or Greece? _____

Review items

10. Fill in the blanks on the time line.

    a. Write **NOW** next to the dot that shows the year now.

    b. Write **2 thousand years ago** next to the right dot.

    c. Write **4 thousand years ago** next to the right dot.

    d. Write **2 hundred years ago** next to the right dot.

    e. Write **1 thousand years ago** next to the right dot.

A ● _____

B ● **1 hundred years ago**

C ● _____

D ● _____

E ● _____

F ● _____

11. **a.** How long ago did the story of Troy take place?

    _____

    b. About how long ago did Jesus Christ live?

    _____

12. How far is it from New York City to San Francisco?

_____

13. **a.** **Fill in the blanks.** If something weighs 1 kilogram, it weighs

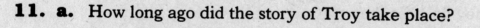

_____ grams.

b. If something weighs 9 kilograms, it weighs _____ grams.

c. How much does a liter of fresh water weigh? _____

14. The words next to each nail tell the color of that nail. Figure out how hot each nail is.
a. Write **1** on the nail that is hottest.
b. Write **2** on the nail that is next-hottest.
c. Write **3** on the nail that is coldest.

15. a. How many shells do coconuts have? _____

b. Is it easy to break open a coconut? _____

c. Tell why. _____

d. What is the juice inside a coconut called? _____

16. The ship in the picture is sinking. It is making currents as it sinks. Make an arrow from each object to show which way it is being pulled.

17. a. In which direction do you fly to get from San Francisco to Japan? _____

b. How far is it from San Francisco to Japan?

_____

c. What ocean do you cross between San Francisco and Japan?

_____

LESSON 86

A

Story items

1. How old was Bertha? _____

2. What kind of school did Bertha go to? _____

3. What was Bertha's talent? _____

4. Who had a better sense of smell, Bertha or a hound dog? _____

5. **a.** Bertha and her friends played Pin the Tail on the Donkey. Did

   any of Bertha's friends pin the tail in the right place? _____

   b. Did Bertha pin the tail in the right place? _____

6. Bertha knew what her friends at the party were doing without

   looking at them. How did she know? _____

7. Name the two things that were in the cans that the school tester used

   to test Bertha's sense of smell. _____

8. Bertha was sorry that she had let people know about her talent. Tell

   why. _____

Skill items

9. Compare Bertha and a hound dog. Remember what you're going to
   tell first and what you're going to tell next.

   _____

   _____

   _____

Review items

10. How far is it from New York City to San Francisco?

    _____

11. **a.** How long did the war between Troy and Greece go on?

    _____

b. What did the Greek army build to help them get inside the wall of Troy? _____

c. Who won the war — Troy or Greece? _____

12. a. What year is it now? _____

b. What was the year 3 hundred years ago? _____

c. Around what year was the first airplane made? _____

d. What was the year 2 hundred years ago? _____

e. What was the year 1 hundred years ago? _____

f. In what year did the United States become a country? _____

g. What year were you born in? _____

h. About how long ago did Jesus Christ live?

_____

i. How long ago did the story of Troy take place?

_____

13. a. How many shells do coconuts have? _____

b. Is it easy to break open a coconut? _____

c. Tell why. _____

d. What is the juice inside a coconut called? _____

14. Fill in the blanks on the time line.

    a. Write **NOW** next to the dot that shows the year now.

    b. Write **2 hundred years ago** next to the right dot.

    c. Write **1 hundred years ago** next to the right dot.

    d. Write **3 thousand years ago** next to the right dot.

    e. Write **2 thousand years ago** next to the right dot.

A   _____

B   _____

C   _____

D   1 thousand years ago

E   _____

F   _____

15. a. In which direction do you fly to get from San Francisco to

    Japan? _____

    b. How far is it from San Francisco to Japan?

    _____

    c. What ocean do you cross between San Francisco and Japan?

    _____

16. The words next to each nail tell the color of that nail. Figure out how hot each nail is.

a. Write **1** on the nail that is hottest.
b. Write **2** on the nail that is next-hottest.
c. Write **3** on the nail that is coldest.

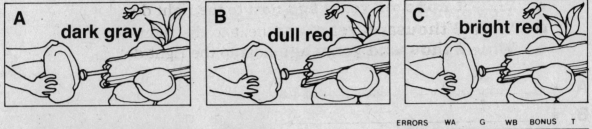

A dark gray
B dull red
C bright red

ERRORS	WA	G	WB	BONUS	T

LESSON 87

A

Story items

1. Bertha became restless after school got out for the summer. Tell

why. _____

2. What is Bonnie Sanchez's job? _____

3. Bonnie said she wasn't a very good investigator. Tell why.

_____

_____

4. Where was the oil company supposed to get its water? _____

5. a. Where did Bonnie think the oil company was getting its water?

_____

b. Could Bonnie prove that what she thought was true? _____

6. How could Bertha help Bonnie? _____

_____

Skill items

7. Compare Bertha and most fourteen-year-old girls. Remember what you're going to tell first and what you're going to tell next.

_____

_____

_____

Review items

8. a. How many legs does an insect have? _____

b. How many legs does a fly have? _____

c. How many legs does a mosquito have? _____

d. How many legs does a goat have? _____

e. How many legs does a spider have? _____

f. How many legs does a water strider have? _____

g. How many legs does an ant have? _____

9. a. What is the temperature inside your body when you are healthy?

_____

b. Fill in the blank. Most fevers don't go over _____ degrees.

c. Name two things that may happen when people have very high

fevers. ① _____

② _____

10. For each contraction below, write the two words that make up the contraction.

CONTRACTION	FIRST WORD	SECOND WORD
a. didn't	_____	_____
b. we'll	_____	_____
c. I've	_____	_____
d. couldn't	_____	_____

11. a. What year is it now? _____

b. What year were you born in? _____

c. How long ago did the story of Troy take place?

_____

d. What was the year 1 hundred years ago? _____

e. What was the year 2 hundred years ago? _____

f. Around what year was the first airplane made? _____

g. What was the year 3 hundred years ago? _____

h. About how long ago did Jesus Christ live?

_____

i. In what year did the United States become a country? _____

12. Let's say that someone in Hohoboho said, "I've **read** that book." **Finish the sentence.** The word that would get the point rhymes

with _____ • fed   • seed

13. The picture below shows a water wheel under a waterfall.
   a. Draw an arrow to show which way A will move.
   b. Start at B and draw an arrow around the shaft to show which way it will turn.
   c. Draw an arrow at C to show which way the vine will move when the shaft turns.

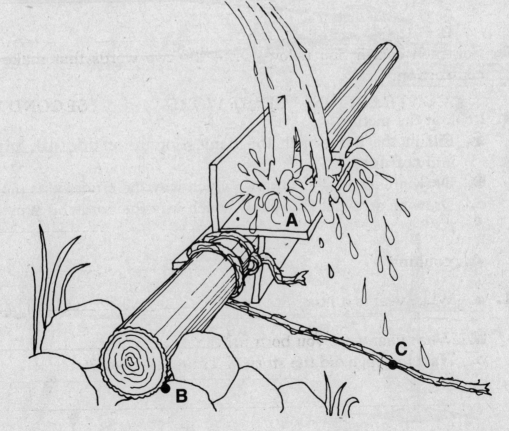

LESSON 88

A

In today's lesson you read about wells. Use what you learned to do these items.

1. Name two kinds of wells. _____

2. Look at the picture. Write these names on the picture to show where each liquid is: **crude oil, fresh water, salt water.**

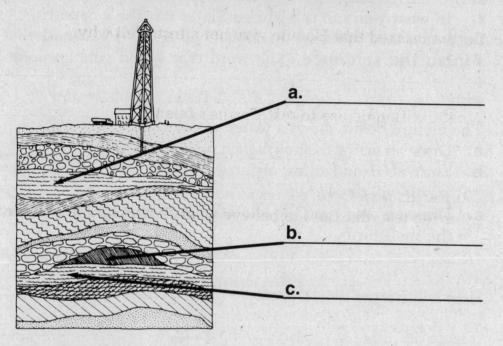

a. _____

b. _____

c. _____

3. Look at the picture.
   a. Fill in the boxes with the names for the **crude oil, pipeline,** and **refinery.**
   b. Draw an arrow at A to show which way the crude oil is moving.
   c. Draw an arrow at B to show which way the crude oil is moving.

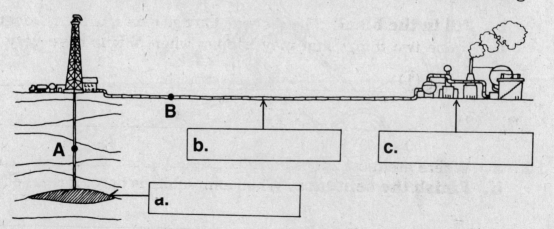

B

Story items

4. Finish the sentence. Gasoline comes from a liquid called

_____

5. When Bertha first told Bonnie about her talent, did Bonnie believe

her? _____

6. Bertha insisted that Bonnie give her a test. Tell why. _____

_____

7. What did Bonnie use to test Bertha's talent? _____

_____

8. Did Bertha pass Bonnie's test? _____
9. After the test, did Bonnie believe what Bertha said about her talent?

_____

10. How will Bertha help Bonnie? _____

_____

Review items

11. a. What is the temperature inside your body when you are

healthy? _____

   b. Fill in the blank. Most fevers don't go over _____ degrees.
   c. Name two things that may happen when people have very high

fevers. ① _____

   ② _____

12. a. Where are mosquitoes born? _____
   b. Finish the sentence. When a mosquito is born, it is called a

_____

c. What do mosquitoes have to do before they can lay eggs?

_____

13. Fill in the blanks on the time line.
    a. Write **NOW** next to the dot that shows the year now.
    b. Write **1 hundred years ago** next to the right dot.
    c. Write **1 thousand years ago** next to the right dot.
    d. Write **2 thousand years ago** next to the right dot.
    e. Write **3 thousand years ago** next to the right dot.

A • _____

B • _____

C • **2 hundred years ago**

D • _____

E • _____

F • _____

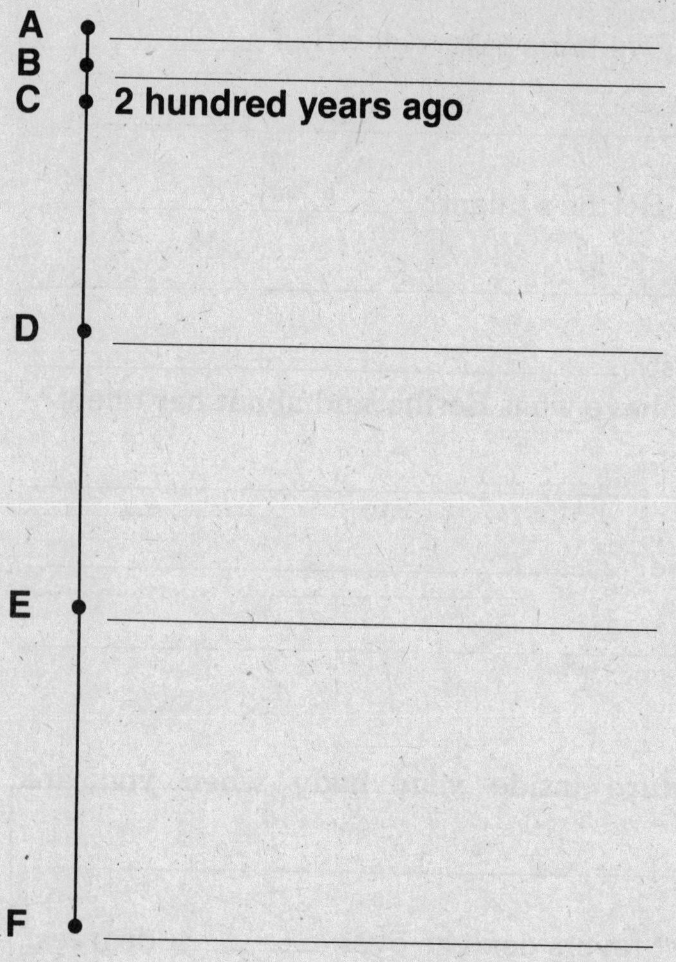

14. Look at the map below.
   a. Write **north, south, east,** and **west** in the right boxes.
   b. Make a **C** where Troy used to be.
   c. Make a **G** where Greece is.

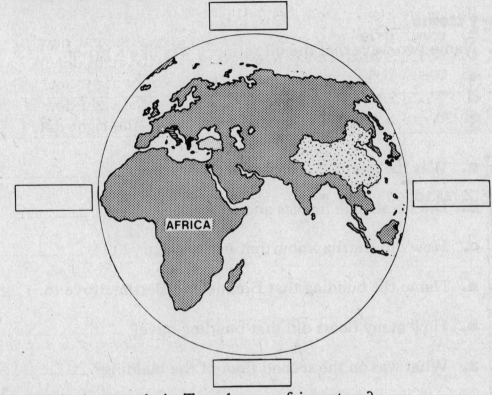

AFRICA

15. Why didn't the people in Troy have refrigerators? _____

_____

16. Look at the picture below.
   a. Make an **F** on the tugboat.
   b. Make an **R** on two docks.
   c. Make a **D** on two ships.

LESSON 89

A

Story items

1. Name two ways that the oil refinery was like a prison.

   ① _____

   ② _____

2. **a.** Was the guard at the gate angry? _____

   b. Did he act like he was angry? _____

   c. How did Bertha know that he was angry? _____

3. **a.** Name the building that Bonnie and Bertha drove to. _____

   b. How many floors did that building have? _____

4. **a.** What was on the second floor of the building? _____

   b. What was on the third floor of the building? _____

5. Bertha smelled something on the third floor that told her who had offices there. What did she smell? **Underline the answer.**
   • lawyers and fish • books • doctors • typists and roast beef

6. What was on the fourth floor of the building? _____

7. How many people did Bertha think worked on the top floor of the

   building? _____

Review items

8. **a.** For how long did the war between Troy and Greece go on?

   _____

   b. What did the Greek army build to help them get inside the

   wall of Troy? _____

   c. Who won the war — Troy or Greece? _____

9. Name two kinds of wells. _____

10. Look at the picture.
  a. Fill in the boxes with the names for the **crude oil, pipeline, and refinery.**
  b. Make an arrow at **X** to show which way the oil is moving.
  c. Make an arrow at **Y** to show which way the oil is moving.

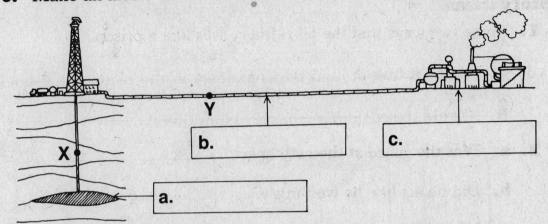

Y

X

b.

c.

a.

11. a. Where are mosquitoes born? _____
  b. **Finish the sentence.** When a mosquito is born, it is called a

  _____

  c. What do mosquitoes have to do before they can lay eggs?

  _____

12. Look at the picture. Write these names in the blanks to show where each liquid is: **crude oil, fresh water, salt water.**

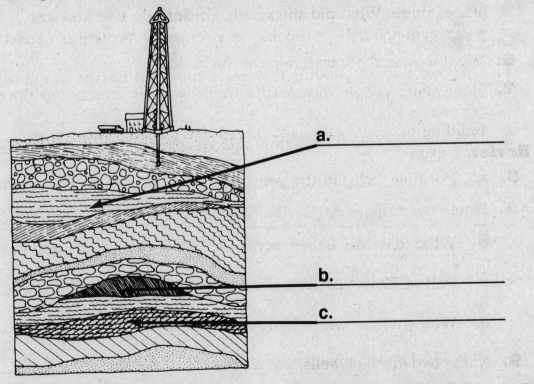

a. _____

b. _____

c. _____

13. Finish the sentence. Gasoline comes from a liquid called

_____

14. Write the letters that are missing for each contraction.

   a. can't _____   **c.** you've _____

   b. we'll _____   **d.** they're _____

15. a. Make a box around the containers in the picture that hold one liter.

   b. Circle the containers that hold four liters.

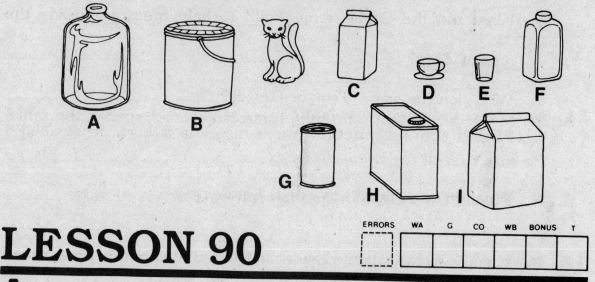

ERRORS	WA	G	CO	WB	BONUS	T

LESSON 90
A

Story items

1. On what floor of building C were Bonnie and Bertha at the beginning

of today's story? _____

2. Name two people that Bonnie and Bertha talked to on the fifth floor.

_____

3. Name two things that Bertha saw in the first office.

_____

4. Name two things that describe what Mr. Daniels looked like.

_____

5. Was Mr. Daniels happy to see Bonnie? _____

6. a. Where was Donna going to take Bonnie and Bertha at the end of

the story? _____

b. Why were they going there? _____

c. Who said that the refinery uses the water in building 9? _____

d. Was that person telling the truth? _____

Review items

7. a. For how long did the war between Troy and Greece go on? ____

b. What did the Greek army build to help them get inside the

wall of Troy? _____

c. Who won the war — Troy or Greece? _____

8. Write two words that sound the same but are not spelled the same.

Be sure to spell the words correctly. _____

9. a. Finish the rule. When things rub together, _____

_____

b. If you rub two sticks together very fast, what will happen to the

sticks? _____

10. a. Fill in the blank. If something weighs 1 kilogram, it weighs

_____ grams.

b. Fill in the blank. If something weighs 4 kilograms, it weighs

_____ grams.

11. a. Look at the picture below. Jar J is filled with ocean water. Jar M

is filled with fresh water. Which jar is heavier? _____

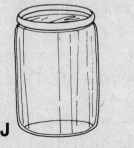 

J   M

b. How much does a liter of fresh water weigh? _____

12. Look at the picture below.
   a. Write **north, south, east,** and **west** in the right boxes.
   b. Write **noon** on the sun you see at noon.
   c. Write **early morning** on the sun you see early in the morning.
   d. Write **evening** on the sun you see in the evening.

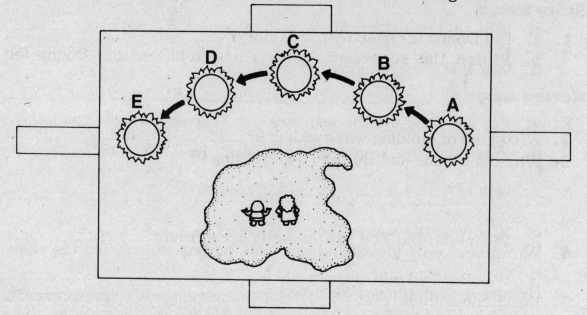

13. Waterfall C is dropping 8 hundred liters of water every second.
Waterfall X is dropping 9 hundred liters of water every second.

Which waterfall has more force? _____

14. a. What does ocean water taste like? _____

   b. What will happen if you drink lots of ocean water? _____

   _____

15. The picture below shows a stream in a streambed.
   a. Where would it be easier to walk, at P or at Q? _____

   b. Tell why. _____

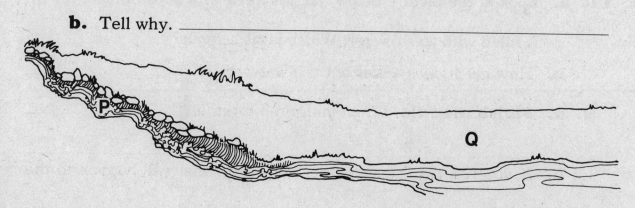

LESSON 91

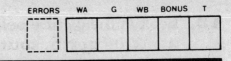

A

Story items

1. **a.** Did Donna act friendly in this story? _____

   b. **Finish the sentence.** Bertha's nose told her that Donna felt

   very _____

2. What kind of building was building 9? _____

3. Why did Bonnie and Bertha go to building 9?

   _____

4. **a.** Where did Big Ted say the water came from? _____

   b. Was Big Ted telling the truth? _____

5. Did Bonnie think that the Reef Oil Company was trying to trick

   her? _____

6. Bonnie and Bertha wanted Mr. Daniels to take them somewhere.

   Tell where. _____

7. Did Mr. Daniels want to do that? _____

Review items

8. **a.** Look at the picture below. Jar A is filled with fresh water. Jar B

   is filled with ocean water. Which jar is heavier? _____

A   B

   b. How much does a liter of fresh water weigh? _____

9. **a.** **Finish the rule.** When things rub together, _____

   _____

   b. If you rub two cans together very fast, what will happen to the

   cans? _____

10. **a.** What year is it now? _____

b. Around what year was the first airplane made? _____

c. What year were you born in? _____

d. What was the year 1 hundred years ago? _____

e. In what year did the United States become a country? _____

f. What was the year 2 hundred years ago? _____

g. About how long ago did Jesus Christ live?

_____

h. What was the year 3 hundred years ago? _____

i. How long ago did the story of Troy take place?

_____

11. **a.** **Fill in the blank.** If something weighs 1 kilogram, it weighs

_____ grams.

b. **Fill in the blank.** If something weighs 8 kilograms, it weighs

_____ grams.

12. **a.** Let's say that someone in Hohoboho said, "**Wind** up your clock." **Finish the sentence.** The word that would get the point

rhymes with _____ • find   • pinned

b. Let's say that someone in Hohoboho said, "I want to **live** in town." **Finish the sentence.** The word that would get the

point rhymes with _____ • hive   • give

13. Why didn't the people in Troy have toasters? _____

_____

LESSON 92

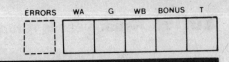

A

Story items

1. Mr. Daniels got Bonnie in trouble with the chief. Tell what Mr. Daniels did. _____

2. Bonnie didn't want the chief to see Bertha when they went to the refinery. Tell why. _____

_____

3. Bertha came up with a plan.

   a. Where did Bertha hide? _____

   b. Where will Bonnie park the car? _____

   c. How will the water get near Bertha? _____

   d. How will Bonnie signal that it is all right for Bertha to talk?

   _____

   e. What will Bertha tell when Bonnie gives the signal?

   _____

4. Bonnie and Bertha did not practice the plan before they left for the refinery. Tell why. _____

5. **a.** How did Bertha feel when the car got to the refinery? _____

   b. How did Bonnie feel? _____

   c. How did the chief feel? _____

6. **a.** Was it comfortable inside the trunk? _____

   b. What made it so hot? _____

   c. Why did Bertha start feeling sick? _____

   _____

Review items

7. For each contraction below, write the two words that make up the contraction.

CONTRACTION	FIRST WORD	SECOND WORD
a. I've	_____	_____
b. we'll	_____	_____
c. aren't	_____	_____

8. The picture below shows a coconut tree. On each line, write the name of the part.

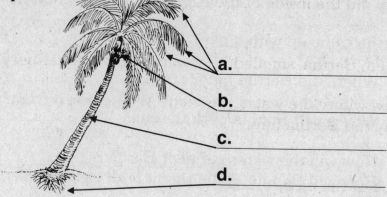

a. _____

b. _____

c. _____

d. _____

9. The picture below shows the parts of a coconut. On each line, write the name of the part.

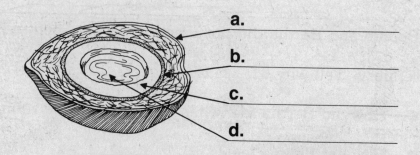

a. _____

b. _____

c. _____

d. _____

10. The picture shows a water wheel under a waterfall.
   a. Draw an arrow to show which way A will move.
   b. Start at B and draw an arrow around the shaft to show which way it will move.
   c. Draw an arrow at C to show which way the vine will move when the shaft turns.

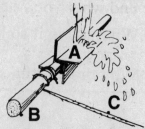

LESSON 93

A

Story items

1. What kind of work was done in building twenty-one?

   _____

2. There was a very strong smell at building twenty-one. What was that

   smell? _____

3. Why did the inside of the trunk keep getting hotter?

   _____

4. When Bertha smelled the water that the refinery was using, she

   knew where the water was from. Where was it from? _____

5. Why did Bertha faint?

   _____

6. Look at the picture below.
   a. Make a **T** on the shadow of the tree.
   b. Make a **C** on the shadow of the car.
   c. Make an **H** on the shadow of the house.

Skill items

7. Compare a beagle and a poodle. Remember what you're going to tell first and what you're going to tell next.

   _____

   _____

   _____

Review items

8. a. Name a state in the United States that is bigger than Italy.

_____

b. Finish the sentence. Italy is shaped something like a _____

9. a. Name three relatives of the word **sit**.

_____

b. Name three relatives of the word **run**.

_____

10. Here is a picture of an ocean liner.

a. Make a **J** on two decks.
b. Make a **K** on two bulkheads.

c. Make a **W** at the prow.
d. Make an **E** at the stern.

11. Look at the map.
   a. Make a **C** where China is.
   b. Make an **I** where Italy is.
   c. Make a **T** where Turkey is.
   d. Make a **J** where Japan is.
   e. Make a **P** where Greece is.
   f. Make a **Y** where Troy used to be.

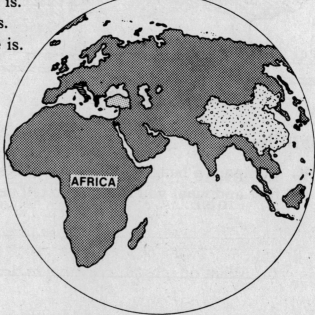

12. The words next to each nail tell the color of the nail. Figure out how hot each nail is.

    a. Write **1** next to the nail that is hottest.

    b. Write **2** next to the nail that is next-hottest.

    c. Write **3** next to the nail that is coldest.

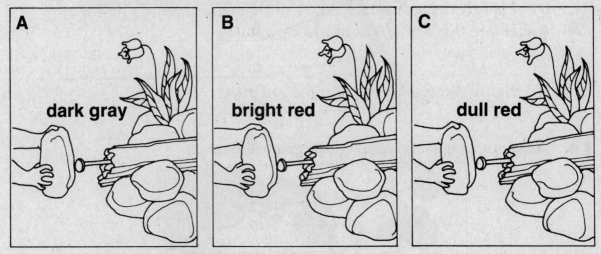

A dark gray   **B** bright red   **C** dull red

13. The picture below shows the parts of a coconut. On each line, write the name of the part.

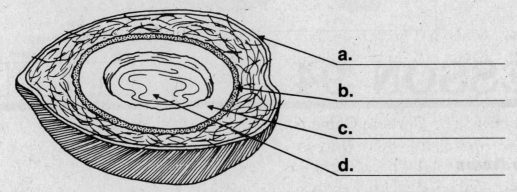

    a. _____

    b. _____

    c. _____

    d. _____

14. Write the letters that are missing for each contraction.

    a. aren't_____   **c.** they're _____

    b. you'll_____   **d.** haven't_____

15. a. Where are mosquitoes born? _____

    b. **Finish the sentence.** When a mosquito is born, it is called a

    _____

    c. What do mosquitoes have to do before they can lay eggs?

    _____

16. The picture below shows a coconut tree. On each line, write the name of the part.

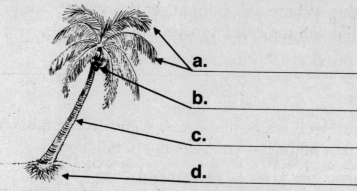

a. _____

b. _____

c. _____

d. _____

17. Make an **I** on each island in the picture below.

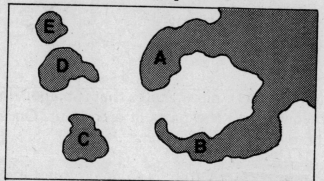

LESSON 94

ERRORS	WA	G	WB	BONUS	T

A

Story items

1. Name two things that Bertha told about the chief to prove her talent.

_____

_____

2. How did Mr. Daniels act while the chief was asking Bertha

questions? _____

3. What did Bertha tell the chief about the water that the refinery was

using? _____

4. The water had something in it that let Bertha know where the water

was from. What was in the water? _____

5. a. At the end of the story, the chief told Bonnie to get six jars of

water. Where will Bonnie get the water? _____

b. What will the chief do with the water?

_____

Skill items

6. Compare well water and creek water. Remember what you're going
to tell first and what you're going to tell next.

_____

_____

_____

Review items

7. a. Name a state in the United States that is bigger than Italy.

_____

b. Finish the sentence. Italy is shaped something like a _____

8. a. Name three relatives of the word **jump.**

_____

b. Name three relatives of the word **eat.**

_____

9. Here is a picture of an ocean liner.

    a. Make a **D** on two decks.   **c.** Make a **P** at the prow.
    b. Make a **B** on two bulkheads.   **d.** Make an **S** at the stern.

10. a. How long did the war between Troy and Greece go on? _____

b. What did the Greek army build to help them get inside the

wall of Troy? _____

_____

c. Who won the war — Troy or Greece? _____

11. Look at the map below.

    a. Make an **A** where China is.

    b. Make a **B** where Italy is.

    c. Make a **C** where Turkey is.

    d. Make a **D** where Japan is.

    e. Make an **E** where Troy used to be.

    f. Make an **F** where Greece is.

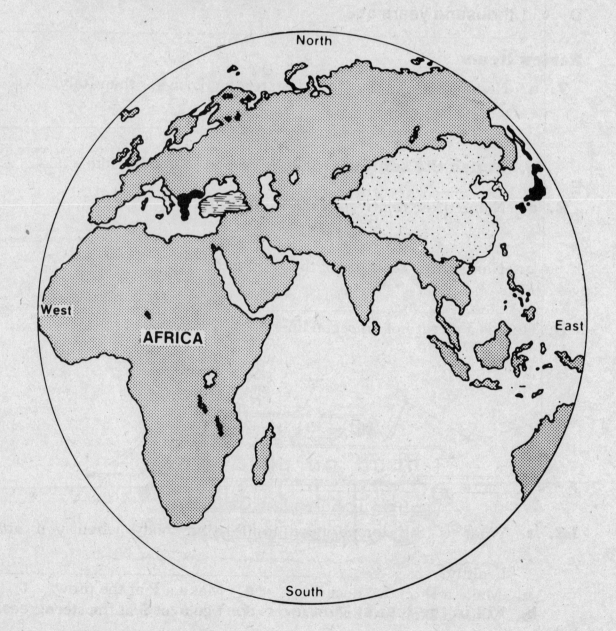

12. Fill in the blanks on the time line.

   a. Write **now** next to the dot that shows the year now.

   b. Write **2 hundred years ago** next to the right dot.

   c. Write **1 hundred years ago** next to the right dot.

   d. Write **4 thousand years ago** next to the right dot.

   e. Write **2 thousand years ago** next to the right dot.

A   _____

B   _____

C   _____

D   **1 thousand years ago**

E   _____

F   _____

13. a. What is the temperature inside your body when you are

    healthy? _____

   b. **Fill in the blank.** Most fevers don't go over _____ degrees.

c. Name two things that may happen when people have very high fevers. _____

_____

14. Look at the picture below.
    a. Make a **G** on the shadow of the dog.
    b. Make an **R** on the shadow of the car.
    c. Make an **E** on the shadow of the tree.

15. Look at the picture below.
    a. **Circle** the containers that hold one liter.
    b. **Cross out** the containers that hold four liters.

A   **B**   **C** **D**   **E**   **F**   **G**   **H**

16. Look at the picture below.
    a. Make a **D** on the tugboat.
    b. Make an **O** on two docks.
    c. Make a **P** on two ships.

LESSON 95

A

Story items

1. How many blindfolds did Bertha have on when she tested the water? _____

2. Name each blindfold. _____

   _____

3. Why did the chief put blindfolds on Bertha? _____

   _____

4. When Bertha tested the water, the chief didn't let her touch the jars of water. Tell why. _____

   _____

5. **a.** How many jars of water did Bertha test? _____

   b. How many jars did she get wrong? _____

6. How did Mr. Daniels act after the test? _____

7. Why did the chief order Mr. Daniels to close the refinery? _____

   _____

8. How did Bertha feel at the end of the story? _____

Review items

9. **a.** What year is it now? _____

   b. What year were you born in? _____

   c. Around what year was the first airplane made? _____

   d. What was the year 1 hundred years ago? _____

   e. What was the year 2 hundred years ago? _____

f. In what year did the United States become a country? _____

g. What was the year 3 hundred years ago? _____

h. How long ago did the story of Troy take place?

_____

i. About how long ago did Jesus Christ live?

_____

10. Name two kinds of wells. _____

11. Finish the sentence. Gasoline comes from a liquid called

_____

12. Waterfall P is dropping 60 liters of water every second. Waterfall M is dropping 40 liters of water every second. Which waterfall has

more force? _____

13. a. Fill in the blanks. If something weighs one kilogram, it weighs

_____ grams.

b. If something weighs 50 kilograms, it weighs _____ grams.

c. How much does a liter of fresh water weigh? _____

14. Fill in the blanks on the time line.
   a. Write NOW next to the dot that shows the year now.
   b. Write **2 hundred years ago** next to the right dot.
   c. Write **1 hundred years ago** next to the right dot.
   d. Write **4 thousand years ago** next to the right dot.
   e. Write **1 thousand years ago** next to the right dot.

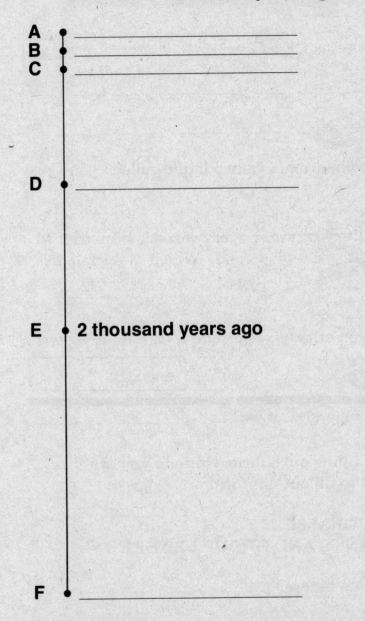

A
B
C

D

E   2 thousand years ago

F

15. a. How long did the war between Troy and Greece go on? _____

   b. What did the Greek army build to help them get inside the

   wall of Troy? _____

   c. Who won the war — Troy or Greece? _____

16. Look at the picture below. Write these names on the picture to show where each liquid is: **crude oil, fresh water, salt water.**

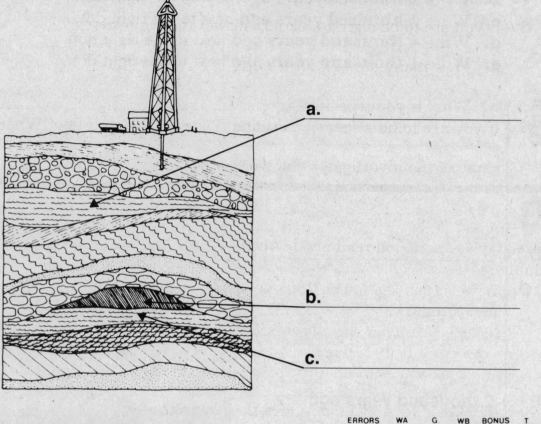

a. _____

b. _____

c. _____

LESSON 96

A

In today's lesson, you read about filling out a form. Pretend you are Bertha and use what you learned to fill out this form.

FORM 80
SPECIAL CONSULTANTS AND GROUP LEADERS

1. Have you worked for the state before? _____

2. How old are you? _____

3. Print your full name. _____
4. Do you want to be a special consultant or a group leader?

_____

5. Do you have your own car? _____

6. How much will you earn every day? _____

7. What is your special talent? _____

8. If you are to be a group leader, answer these questions:

    a. How many are in your group? _____

    b. What is your special topic? _____

9. If you are to be a special consultant, answer this question: What's the

name of the investigator you work with? _____

B

In today's lesson, you read about Achilles' heel. Use what you learned to do these items.

10. Write each sentence below using other words for the word **weakness.**

    a. His left hand was his **weakness.** _____

    _____

    b. Their love of money was their **weakness.** _____

    _____

C

Story items

11. a. Where did Achilles' mother take him when he was a baby?

    _____

    b. Why did she want to dip him in the river?

    _____

12. a. Finish the rule about the water in the river. If the water

touched a part of your body, _____

    _____

    b. If you put your arm in the magic river, what would happen to

your arm? _____

13. Achilles' mother held on to part of him when she dipped him in the

river. What part? _____

14. What part of Achilles did not get wet? _____

15. What part of Achilles could get hurt? _____

16. What army was Achilles in? _____
17. Why were all the soldiers afraid of Achilles?

_____

18. Is the story about Achilles a true story? _____

Review items

19. Write two words that sound the same but are not spelled the same.

Be sure to spell the words correctly. _____

LESSON 97

ERRORS	WA	G	WB	BONUS	T

A

In today's lesson you read about homonyms. Use what you learned to do these items.

1. Finish the sentence. A word that sounds the same as another

word is called a _____

2. Write a homonym for each word below.

a. four _____ **e.** to _____

b. ate _____ **f.** there _____

c. new _____ **g.** rode _____

d. hear _____ **h.** won _____

3. In the sentence below, **underline** each word that has a homonym.

I knew that he won four races.

B

In today's lesson, you read about chariots. Use what you learned to do these items.

4. Look at the picture below.

   a. What is the name of the vehicle in the picture? _____

   b. How many wheels does the vehicle have? _____

   c. What is pulling the vehicle? _____

   d. What is soldier A doing? _____

   e. What is soldier B doing? _____

Soldier A

Soldier B

C

Story items

5. How many ships went to war with Troy? _____

6. Which army was Achilles in? _____

7. How long was Achilles in the war with Troy? _____

8. Who was the greatest soldier of Troy? _____

9. Who won when Achilles and Hector fought? _____

10. Finish the sentence. Achilles rode around the wall of Troy in a

_____

11. How did the people of Troy feel when Achilles killed Hector?

_____

12. Did the arrows that hit Achilles in the chest hurt him? _____

13. a. Finish the sentence. The arrow that killed Achilles hit him in

the _____

b. Did that arrow kill Achilles because it made a very bad cut in

him? _____

c. That arrow had something on it that killed Achilles. What did it

have on it? _____

Review items

14. The picture shows a water wheel under a waterfall.
   a. Draw an arrow to show which way A will move.
   b. Start at B and draw an arrow around the shaft to show which
   way it will move.
   c. Draw an arrow at C to show
   which way the vine will move
   when the shaft turns.

15. Look at the picture below.
   a. Fill in the boxes with the names for the **crude oil, pipeline,**
   and **refinery.**
   b. Draw an arrow at X to show which way the crude oil is moving.
   c. Draw an arrow at Y to show which way the crude oil is moving.

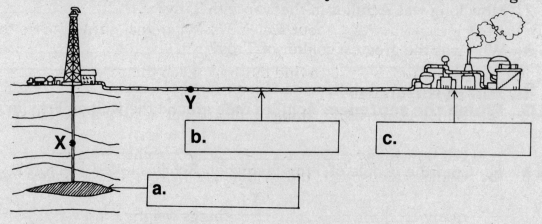

16. Tell how many legs each thing has.

    a. ant _____

    b. water strider _____

    c. spider _____

    d. flea _____

    e. mosquito _____

    f. fly _____

    g. insect _____

17. Why didn't the people in Troy have televisions? _____
_____

18. a. Finish the rule. When things rub together, _____
_____

    b. If you rub two nails together very fast, what will happen to the

    nails? _____

19. a. When a boy jumps this way ↗, there is a push against the

    ground. Draw an arrow to show the direction of that push. _____

    b. If a girl dove into a pool in this direction ↖, there would be a
    push against the side of the pool. Draw an arrow to show the

    direction of that push. _____

LESSON 98

ERRORS	WA	G	WB	BONUS	T

A

In today's lesson you read about scales. Use what you learned to do these items.

    1. Name the tool we use to find out how much things weigh. _____

    2. Fill in the blanks.

        a. Some scales weigh things that are not very heavy. These scales

        tell how many _____ things weigh.

        b. Some scales weigh things that are heavy. These scales tell how

        many _____ things weigh.

3. The scales in picture A tell about **grams.** Fill in the blanks to tell how many grams each object weighs.

a. _____   b. _____   c. _____

PICTURE A

4. The scales in picture B tell about **kilograms.** Fill in the blanks to tell how many kilograms each object weighs.

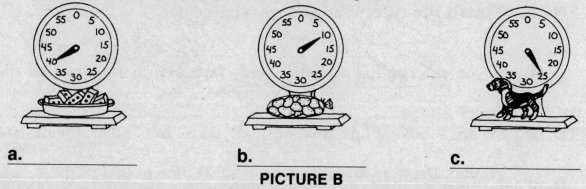

a. _____   b. _____   c. _____

PICTURE B

B

Story items

5. Sid was going to jump from the canoe to the dock.

a. How far was it from the canoe to the dock? _____

b. Did Sid's dad think Sid would end up on the dock? _____

c. Where did Sid end up when he jumped? _____

6. Finish the rule. When something moves in one direction, _____

_____

7. a. What did the needle on the scale point to when Sid was standing

still? _____

b. What did the needle on the scale point to when Sid jumped up?

_____

8. Sid is going to jump from the canoe to the dock.

    a. Make a dotted arrow on Sid to show which way he will jump.

    b. Make a solid arrow on the back of the canoe to show which way it will move.

9. The picture below shows Sid on a scale.

    a. Draw a dotted arrow on Sid to show which way he will move when he jumps up.

    b. Draw a solid arrow on the bottom of the scale to show the push in the opposite direction.

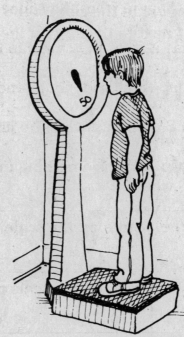

Review items

10. Look at the picture below.

    a. What is the name of the vehicle in the picture? _____

    b. How many wheels does the vehicle have? _____

    c. What is pulling the vehicle? _____

    d. What is soldier T doing? _____

    e. What is soldier J doing? _____

11. Finish the sentence. A word that sounds the same as another

word is called a _____

12. Look at the map.

    a. Write **east** next to the city on the east coast.

    b. Write **west** next to the city on the west coast.

    c. Draw an arrow to show the trip from New York City to San Francisco.

    d. Make a **B** where Denver is.

    e. Make an **I** where Chicago is.

    f. Make an **F** where Salt Lake City is.

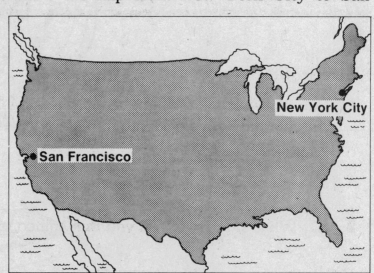

13. Look at the picture. The man is holding a stick that is one meter long.

    a. Write the letter of each object that is one meter long. _____

    b. Write the letter of each object that is two meters long. _____

14. Write a homonym for each word below.

    a. eight _____   **d.** knew _____

    b. two _____   **e.** rode _____

    c. won _____

LESSON 99

ERRORS	WA	G	WB	BONUS	T

A

Story items

1. People who lived 80 thousand years ago did not have many things that we have today. Name four things they did not have.

_____

_____

2. a. What clue could tell you that someone ate chicken?

_____

b. What clue could tell you that someone ate coconut?

_____

3. What's a good place to look for clues about people? _____

4. People who lived 80 thousand years ago did not have houses like we

have. **Finish the sentence.** Some of those people lived in _____

5. There are clues that tell us that dogs may have lived with people

8 thousand years ago. What clues? _____

_____

6. There are clues that tell us how people may have hunted large animals like buffalo. What clues?

_____

7. What clues would tell us that people used fire to cook their food?

_____

8. Did the first people who lived in caves cook their food? _____

Review items

9. Look at the picture below.
   a. What is the name of the vehicle in the picture? _____

   b. How many wheels does the vehicle have? _____

   c. What is pulling the vehicle? _____

   d. What is soldier X doing? _____

   e. What is soldier Y doing? _____

Soldier X   **Soldier Y**

10. Write two words that sound the same but are not spelled the same.

Be sure to spell the words correctly. _____

11. Tell how many legs each thing has.

a. fly _____   **e.** water strider _____

b. sheep _____   **f.** ant _____

c. flea _____   **g.** insect _____

d. spider _____

12. For each contraction below, write the two words that make up the contraction.

CONTRACTION	FIRST WORD	SECOND WORD
a. we're	_____	_____
b. she'll	_____	_____
c. shouldn't	_____	_____
d. you've	_____	_____

13. Some lines in the box below are not one centimeter long. **Cross out** the lines that are not one centimeter long.

14. Look at the picture. The man is holding a stick that is one meter long.

a. Write the letter of each object that is one meter long. _____

b. Write the letter of each object that is two meters long. _____

15. The scales in the picture tell about **grams.** Fill in the blanks to tell how many grams each object weighs.

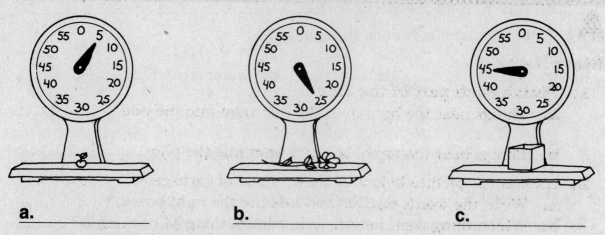

a. _____   b. _____   c. _____

16. Look at the map below.
  a. Write **east** next to the city on the east coast.
  b. Write **west** next to the city on the west coast.
  c. Draw an arrow to show the trip from New York City to San Francisco.
  d. Make a **B** where Denver is.
  e. Make a **V** where Chicago is.
  f. Make an **F** where Salt Lake City is.

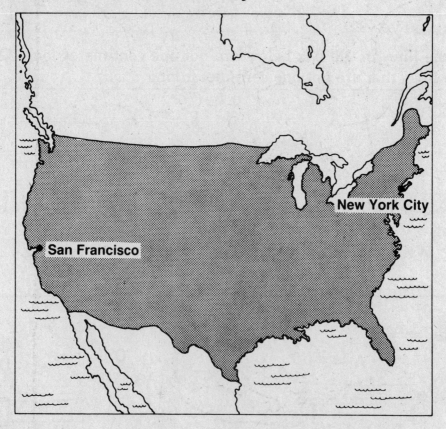

17. Name the tool we use to find out how much things weigh. _____

LESSON 100

A

Story items

1. **Finish each part of the rule.**
   a. Things near the bottom of the pile went into the pile _____

   b. Things near the top of the pile went into the pile _____

2. Look at the picture below. It shows a pile of garbage.
   a. Write the words **earlier** and **later** in the right boxes.
   b. Which thing went into the pile earlier, thing M or thing B? _____

   c. Which thing went into the pile earlier, thing A or thing S? _____

   d. Which thing went into the pile later, thing A or thing B? _____

   e. Which thing went into the pile later, thing M or thing R? _____

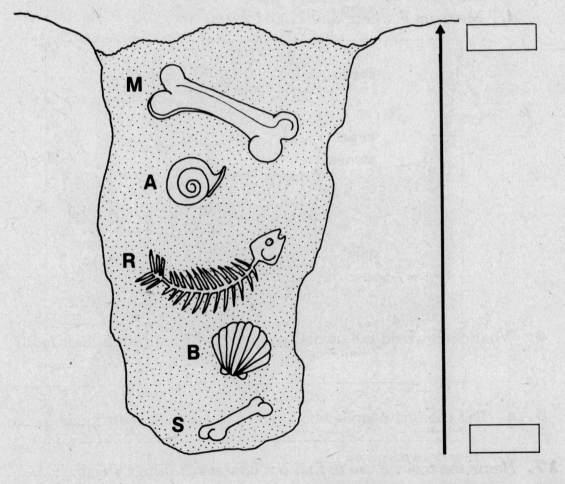

3. Look at the picture below. It shows a hole dug near a beach.

   a. When we dig into the pile, what's the first thing we find?

   _____

   b. What's the next thing we find? _____

   c. What's the next thing we find? _____

   d. What's the next thing we find? _____

   e. What's the last thing we find? _____

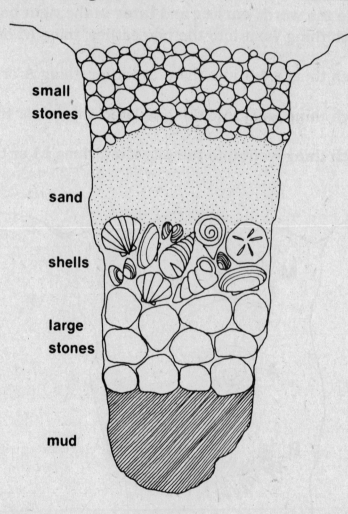

small
stones

sand

shells

large
stones

mud

4. What clues would tell us that people used fire to cook their food?

_____

5. a. Did the first people who lived in caves cook their food? _____

   b. How do we know? _____

Review items

6. People who lived 80 thousand years ago did not have many things that we have today. Name four things they did not have.

_____

7. a. What clue could tell you that someone ate coconut?

_____

b. What clue could tell you that someone ate chicken?

_____

8. People who lived 80 thousand years ago did not have houses like we have. **Finish the sentence.** Some of those people lived in

_____

9. For each contraction below, write the two words that make up the contraction.

CONTRACTION	FIRST WORD	SECOND WORD
a. we've	_____	_____
b. couldn't	_____	_____
c. I'll	_____	_____
d. aren't	_____	_____

10. a. Where are mosquitoes born? _____

b. **Finish the sentence.** When a mosquito is born, it is called a

_____

c. What do mosquitoes have to do before they can lay eggs?

_____

11. **Fill in the blanks.**

a. Some scales weigh things that are heavy. These scales tell how

many _____ things weigh.

b. Some scales weigh things that are not very heavy. These scales

tell how many _____ things weigh.

12. Look at the picture below.
  a. Make a **T** on the shadow of the dog.
  b. Make a **C** on the shadow of the house.
  c. Make an **H** on the shadow of the car.
  d. Make a **D** on the shadow of the tree.

13. Some lines in the box below are one centimeter long. **Circle** the lines that are one centimeter long.

14. Let's say that someone in Hohoboho said, "Last week I **read** two books." **Finish the sentence.** The word that would get the point

rhymes with _____ • bed • feed

15. The scales in the picture tell about **kilograms.** Fill in the blanks to tell how many kilograms each object weighs.

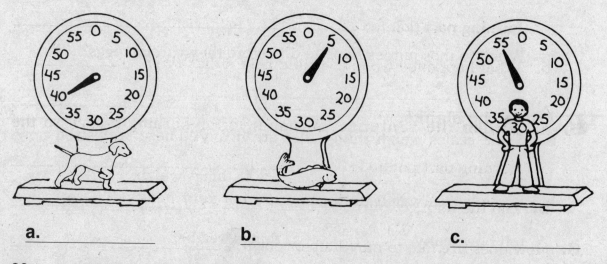

a. _____ b. _____ c. _____

LESSON 101

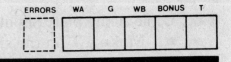

A
Story items

1. Finish each part of the rule.
   a. Things near the bottom of the pile _____

_____

   b. Things near the top of the pile _____

_____

2. The people who lived 80 thousand years ago did not live like we do.
   a. Finish the sentence. The people wore clothes made from

_____

   b. Name two things the people used to kill animals. _____

_____

   c. Where did the people live? _____

   d. When did the people move to a new cave?

_____

3. a. What makes the sound of thunder? _____

   b. Which comes first, lightning or thunder? _____

4. a. Finish the sentence. A child held the burning branch so the

burning part pointed _____

   b. What happened when the child held it that way? _____

_____

5. a. Finish the sentence. A man held the burning branch so the

burning part pointed _____

   b. Did the man get burned? _____

6. How does fire like to move, up or down? _____

7. How did the people in the cave feel about the fire? _____

_____

Skill items

8. Compare a cave to a house. Remember what you're going to tell first and what you're going to tell next.

_____

_____

_____

Review items

9. a. What clues would tell us that people used fire to cook their

food? _____

   b. Did the people who first lived in caves cook their food? _____

   c. How do we know? _____

_____

10. Look at the picture below. It shows a pile of garbage.
   a. Write the words **earlier** and **later** in the right boxes.
   b. Which thing went into the pile earlier, thing M or thing A? _____
   c. Which thing went into the pile earlier, thing B or thing R? _____

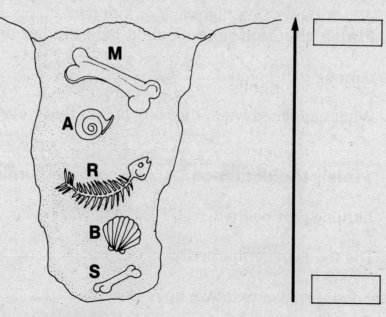

d. Which thing went into the pile later, thing S or thing B? _____

e. Which thing went into the pile later, thing A or thing R? _____

11. a. Where are mosquitoes born? _____
b. Finish the sentence. When a mosquito is born, it is called a

_____

c. What do mosquitoes have to do before they can lay eggs?

_____

12. Look at the picture below. It shows a hole dug near a beach.
a. When we dig into the pile, what's the first thing we find?

_____

b. What's the next thing we find? _____

c. What's the next thing we find? _____

d. What's the next thing we find? _____

e. What's the last thing we find? _____

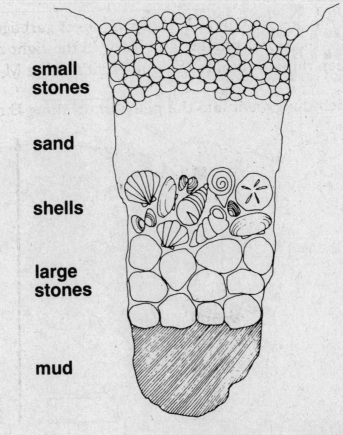

small
stones

sand

shells

large
stones

mud

13. Look at the picture below. Write these names in the blanks to show where each liquid is: **crude oil**   **fresh water**   **salt water**

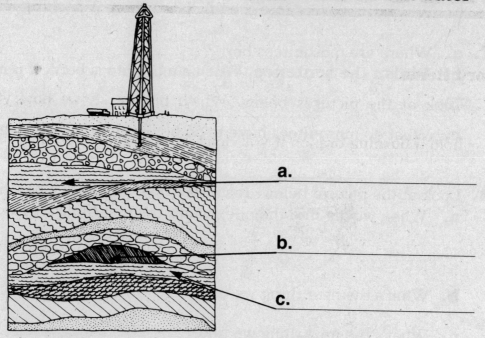

a. _____

b. _____

c. _____

14. Look at the map below.
   a. Write **north, south, east,** and **west** in the right boxes.
   b. Make an **X** where Troy used to be.
   c. Make an **L** where Greece is.
   d. Make a **K** where Japan is.
   e. Make a **Z** where Italy is.
   f. Make a **B** where China is.
   g. Make an **A** where Turkey is.

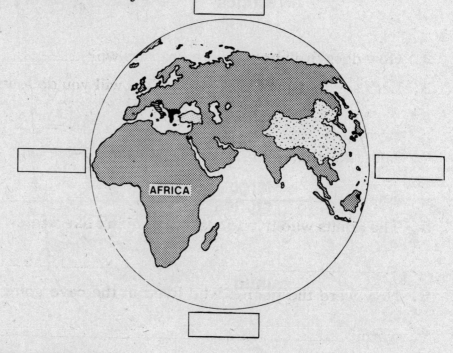

AFRICA

LESSON 102

A

Story items

1. Look at the pictures below. Which picture shows how you should

hold a burning branch if you don't want to get burned? _____

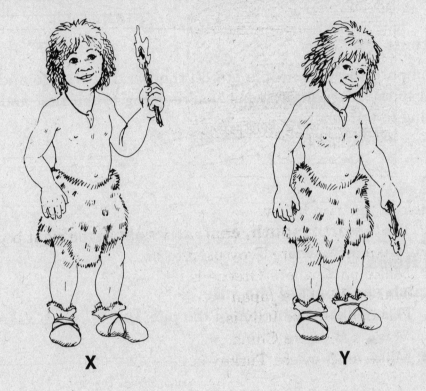

X   Y

2. How does fire like to move, up or down? _____

3. Let's say that Jack stands up. What will you do to imitate Jack?

_____

4. Let's say that Jean hops on one foot. What will you do to imitate

Jean? _____

5. The adults who lived in the cave didn't like winter. Tell why.

_____

6. How were the people who lived in the cave going to keep the cave

warm? _____

7. Look at the picture.

    a. Write **north, south, east,** and **west** in the right boxes.

    b. The wind blows from the north. Draw an arrow from the dot to show that wind.

    c. **Circle** every person who is facing north.

    d. The man waves his fist at the wind. Write **M** on that man.

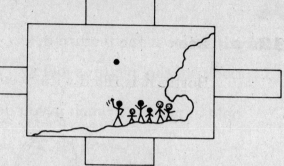

Skill items

8. Compare the way people ate 80 thousand years ago and the way we eat today. Remember what you're going to tell first and what you're going to tell next.

_____

_____

_____

Review items

9. Finish each part of the rule.

    a. Things near the bottom of the pile _____

    _____

    b. Things near the top of the pile _____

    _____

10. Fill in the blanks.

    a. If something weighs 1 kilogram, it weighs _____ grams.

    b. If something weighs 6 kilograms, it weighs _____ grams.

    c. If something weighs 3 kilograms, it weighs _____ grams.

11. The people who lived 80 thousand years ago did not live like we do.

    a. What did the people make their clothes from? _____

    b. Name two things the people used to kill animals. _____

    _____

c. Where did the people live? _____

d. When did the people move to a new cave? _____

_____

12. a. Look at the picture below. Bottle J is filled with fresh water.

Bottle K is filled with ocean water. Which bottle is heavier? _____

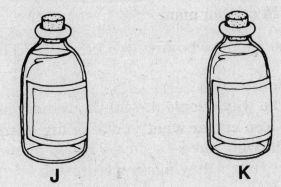

J   K

b. How much does a liter of fresh water weigh? _____

13. Finish the rule. When things rub together, _____

_____

14. a. What makes the sound of thunder? _____

b. Which comes first, lightning or thunder? _____

15. Name two kinds of wells. _____

16. Finish the sentence. Gasoline comes from a liquid called

_____

17. a. Underline the containers in the picture below that hold one liter.

b. Circle the containers that hold four liters.

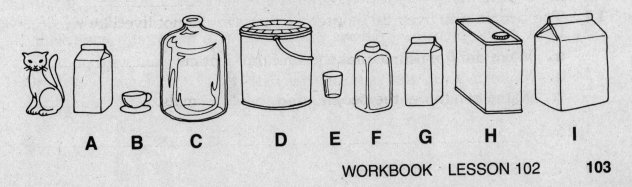

A   B   C   D   E   F   G   H   I

LESSON 103

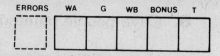

A

Story items

1. a. What clues would tell us that people used fire to cook their food?

_____

b. Did the people who first lived in caves cook their food? _____

c. How do we know? _____

_____

2. The people who lived in caves drew pictures on the cave walls. Name three things they made pictures of.

_____

3. Look at the picture below.

a. Name one thing you can tell about hand A. _____

b. Name one thing you can tell about hand B. _____

c. Name two ways that hand A is different from hand C.

_____

_____

A   B   C

4. Name three things that cave people used to make paint.

_____

5. Look at the picture. It shows the outline of a hand on a cave wall.
a. Make an **X** on the part of the wall that was covered with paint.
b. Make a **Y** on the part of the wall that was not covered with paint.

6. Cave people painted pictures of horses on cave walls. How are those

horses different from horses that live today? _____

7. Some kinds of animals that lived thousands of years ago are not alive

today. How do we know what those animals looked like? _____

_____

Review items

8. Fill in the blanks.

   a. If something weighs 1 kilogram, it weighs _____ grams.

   b. If something weighs 9 kilograms, it weighs _____ grams.

9. Look at the pictures below. Which picture shows how you should

hold a burning branch if you don't want to get burned? _____

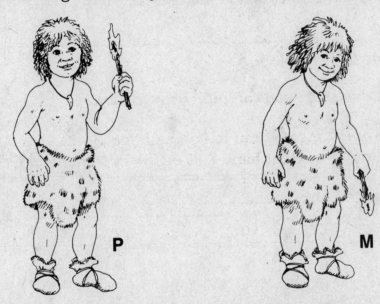

P   M

10. a. Look at the picture below. Bottle M is filled with ocean water.

Bottle Z is filled with fresh water. Which bottle is heavier? _____

M   Z

   b. How much does a liter of fresh water weigh? _____

11. a. Finish the rule. When things rub together, _____

_____

b. If you rub two rocks together very fast, what will happen to the

rocks? _____

12. Finish the sentence. A word that sounds the same as another

word is called a _____

13. Look at the picture below.

   a. Fill in the boxes with the names for the **pipeline, refinery,** and **crude oil.**

   b. Draw an arrow at **X** to show which way the crude oil is moving.

   c. Draw an arrow at **Y** to show which way the crude oil is moving.

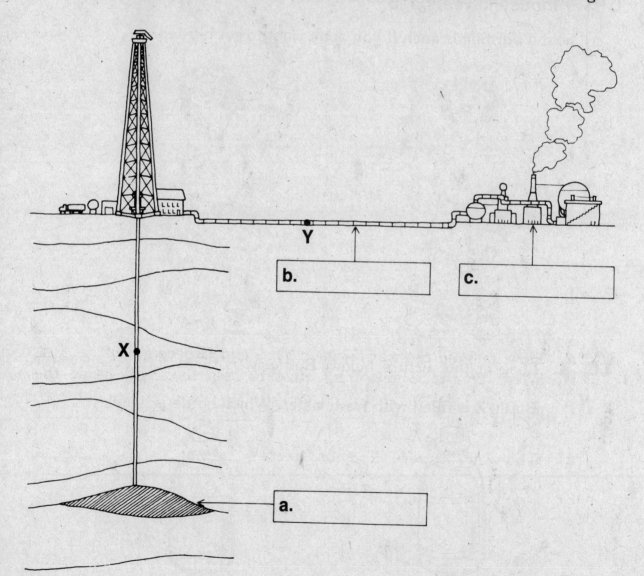

14. Fill in the blanks on the time line below.

  a. Write **NOW** next to the dot that shows the year now.
  b. Write **2 hundred years ago** next to the right dot.
  c. Write **3 thousand years ago** next to the right dot.
  d. Write **1 hundred years ago** next to the right dot.
  e. Write **2 thousand years ago** next to the right dot.

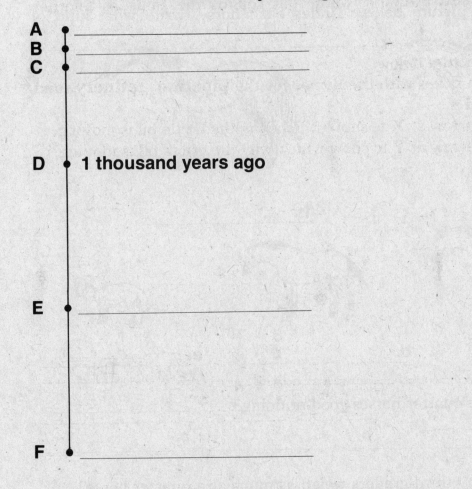

A
B _____
C _____

D • **1 thousand years ago**

E _____

F _____

15. a. How long did the war between Troy and Greece go on? _____
  b. What did the Greek army build to help them get inside the

  wall of Troy? _____

  c. Who won the war — Troy or Greece? _____

LESSON 104

ERRORS WA G WB BONUS T

A

Story items

1. Look at the picture below. Under each horse, write what kind of horse is shown.

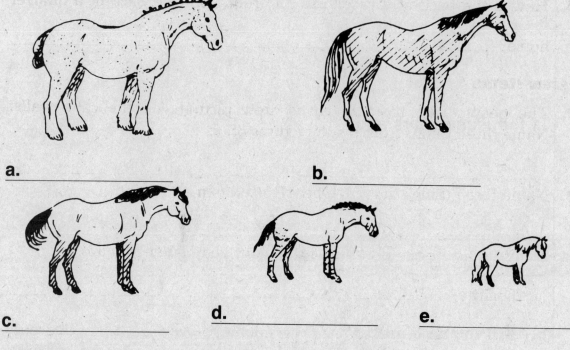

a. _____   b. _____

c. _____   d. _____   e. _____

2. **a.** What are quarter horses good at doing? _____

_____

   b. How many third-graders weigh as much as a quarter horse? _____

3. **a.** What are draft horses good at doing? _____

   b. How many third-graders weigh as much as a draft horse? _____

4. **a. Finish the sentence with words from the story.** The

   Mongolian horse was the kind of horse that lived _____ thousand years ago.

   b. How many third-graders weigh as much as a Mongolian horse?

_____

5. **a.** What are racehorses good at doing? _____

   b. How tall is a racehorse at the head? _____

c. How many third-graders weigh as much as a racehorse? _____

6. a. How tall is a pony at the shoulder? _____

b. How many third-graders weigh as much as a pony? _____

7. How are the legs of a racehorse different from the legs of a draft

horse? _____

8. How is the back of a racehorse different from the back of a quarter

horse? _____

Review items

9. The people who lived in caves drew pictures on the cave walls. Name three things they made pictures of.

_____

10. Name three things that cave people used to make paint.

_____

11. a. What is the temperature inside your body when you are

healthy? _____

b. Fill in the blank. Most fevers don't go over _____ degrees.

c. Name two things that may happen when people have very high

fevers. _____

12. a. Cave people painted pictures of horses on cave walls. How are those horses different from horses that live today?

_____

b. Some kinds of animals that lived thousands of years ago are not alive today. How do we know what those animals looked like?

_____

13. Look at the map.

    a. Write **north, south, east,** and **west** in the right boxes.

    b. Make a **T** where New York City is.

    c. Make an **H** where San Francisco is.

    d. Make an **R** where Japan is.

    e. Make an **F** where the Pacific Ocean is.

LESSON 105

A

Story items

1. The people who lived in caves drew pictures on the cave walls. Name three things they made pictures of.

_____

2. Finish each part of the rule.

    a. Things near the bottom of the pile _____

    b. Things near the top of the pile _____

3. Look at picture 1.

    a. Write the words **earlier** and **later** in the right boxes.

    b. How many years ago did layer A go into the pile? _____

    c. How many years ago did layer B go into the pile? _____

    d. How many years ago did layer C go into the pile? _____

    e. How many years ago did layer D go into the pile? _____

    f. How many years ago did layer E go into the pile? _____

4. Look at picture 1. **Finish each sentence.**

    a. The horse skeleton in layer A is no bigger than _____

    b. The horse skeleton in layer B is about as big as _____

    c. The horse skeleton in layer C is about as big as _____

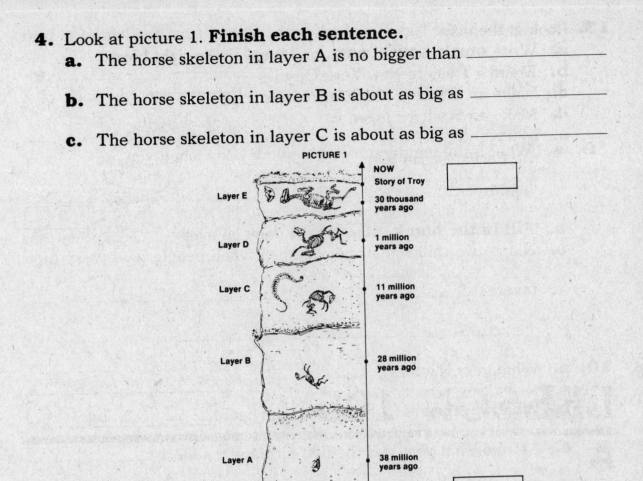

PICTURE 1

NOW
Story of Troy

Layer E — 30 thousand years ago

Layer D — 1 million years ago

Layer C — 11 million years ago

Layer B — 28 million years ago

Layer A — 38 million years ago

5. How was the earliest horse different from horses that live today?

_____

6. The earliest horses on earth are not alive today. How long ago did

the earliest horses live? _____

Review items

    7. Look at the picture. Under each horse, write
    what kind of horse is shown.

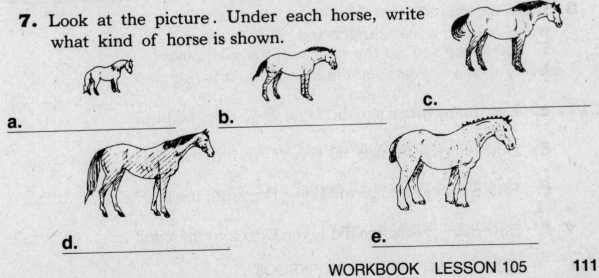

a. _____ **b.** _____ **c.** _____

d. _____ **e.** _____

8. a. How are the legs of a racehorse different from the legs of a draft

horse? _____

b. How is the back of a racehorse different from the back of a

quarter horse? _____

9. a. What is the temperature inside your body when you are

healthy? _____

b. Fill in the blank. Most fevers don't go over _____ degrees.

c. Name two things that may happen when people have very high

fevers. _____

_____

10. a. What year is it now? _____

b. What was the year 1 hundred years ago? _____

c. Around what year was the first airplane made? _____

d. What year were you born in? _____

e. About how long ago did Jesus Christ live?

_____

f. In what year did the United States become a country? _____

g. What was the year 3 hundred years ago? _____

h. What was the year 2 hundred years ago? _____

i. How long ago did the story of Troy take place?

_____

11. Look at the picture.

a. Which rabbit is going faster? _____

b. How fast is that rabbit going? _____

c. Which car is going faster? _____

d. How fast is that car going? _____

e. Which truck is going faster? _____

f. How fast is that truck going? _____

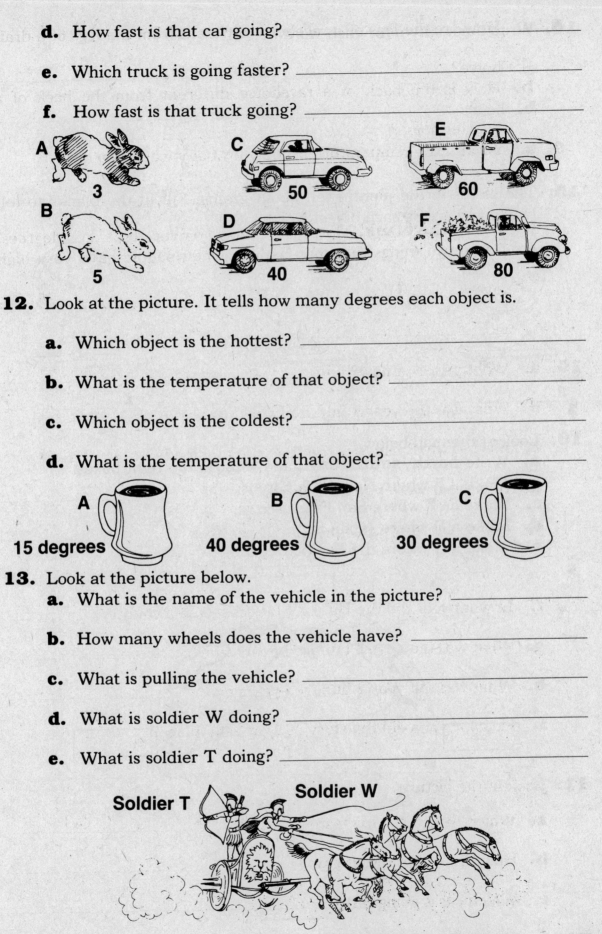

A 3

B 5

C 50

D 40

E 60

F 80

12. Look at the picture. It tells how many degrees each object is.

a. Which object is the hottest? _____

b. What is the temperature of that object? _____

c. Which object is the coldest? _____

d. What is the temperature of that object? _____

A 15 degrees

B 40 degrees

C 30 degrees

13. Look at the picture below.
a. What is the name of the vehicle in the picture? _____

b. How many wheels does the vehicle have? _____

c. What is pulling the vehicle? _____

d. What is soldier W doing? _____

e. What is soldier T doing? _____

Soldier T   Soldier W

14. Write a homonym for each word below.

    a. too _____

    b. hear _____

    c. ate _____

    d. four _____

    e. one _____

15. The scales in the picture tell about grams. Fill in the blanks to tell how many grams each object weighs.

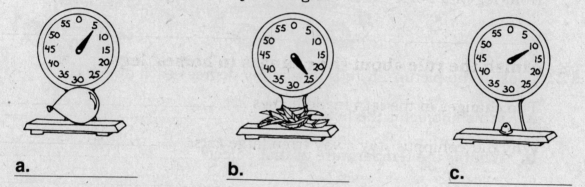

  a. _____   **b.** _____   **c.** _____

16. Look at the map below.
    a. Write **north, south, east,** and **west** in the right boxes.
    b. Make a **B** where New York City is.
    c. Make an **F** where San Francisco is.
    d. Make a **D** where Japan is.
    e. Make a **G** where the Pacific Ocean is.

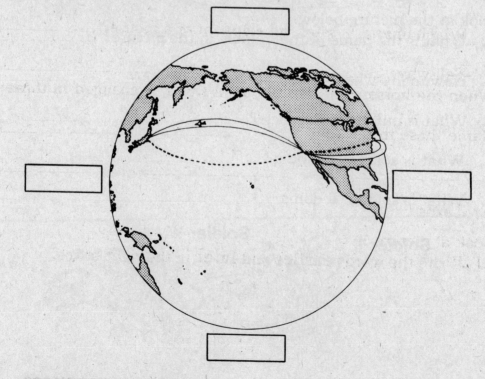

LESSON 106

A

Story items

1. **Fill in the blank.** Eohippus lived _____ million years ago.

2. Name two ways that the front leg of eohippus was different from the front leg of a horse that lives today. _____

    _____

3. **Finish the rule about the changes in horses' legs.**

    The changes in the legs made horses _____

4. Why did eohippus stay away from large cats? _____

    _____

5. Over millions of years, horses changed in size. What happened to the size of the horses? _____

6. Why are bigger animals safer? _____

    _____

7. **a.** Which animal is safer, an elephant or a mouse? _____

    b. Tell why. _____

8. When the horse went into the open fields, it changed in three ways.

    Name those three ways. _____

    _____

Review items

9. Look at picture 1.
    a. Write the words **earlier** and **later** in the right boxes.

b. How many years ago did layer A go into the pile? _____

c. How many years ago did layer B go into the pile? _____

d. How many years ago did layer C go into the pile? _____

e. How many years ago did layer D go into the pile? _____

f. How many years ago did layer E go into the pile? _____

10. Look at picture 1. **Finish each sentence.**

a. The horse skeleton in layer A is no bigger than _____

b. The horse skeleton is layer B is about as big as _____

c. The horse skeleton in layer C is about as big as _____

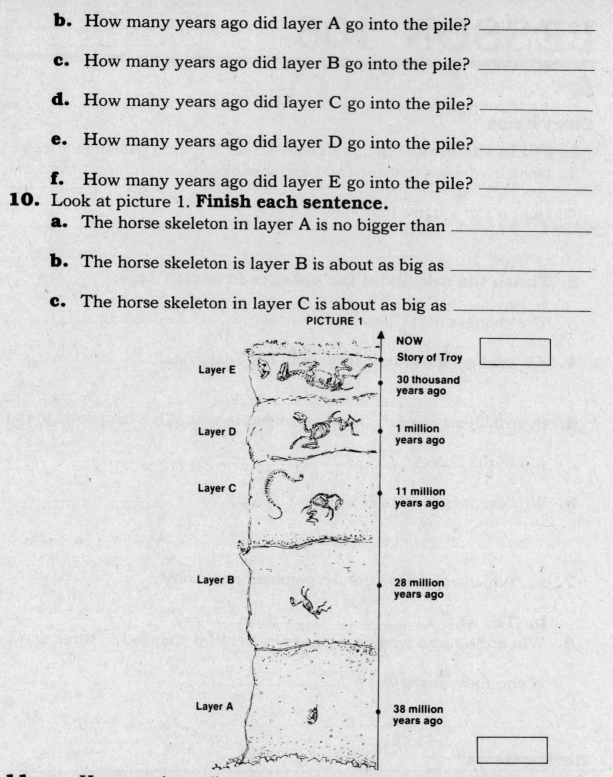

PICTURE 1

NOW
Story of Troy

Layer E   30 thousand
                 years ago

Layer D   1 million
                 years ago

Layer C   11 million
                 years ago

Layer B   28 million
                 years ago

Layer A   38 million
                 years ago

11. a. How was the earliest horse different from horses that live today?

_____

b. The earliest horses on earth are not alive today. How long ago

did the earliest horses live? _____

12. a. What year is it now? _____

   b. What year were you born in? _____

   c. Around what year was the first airplane made? _____

   d. What was the year 1 hundred years ago? _____

   e. What was the year 2 hundred years ago? _____

   f. In what year did the United States become a country? _____

   g. What was the year 3 hundred years ago? _____

   h. About how long ago did Jesus Christ live?

   _____

   i. How long ago did the story of Troy take place?

   _____

13. Look at the pictures below. Which picture shows you how you should

   hold a burning branch if you don't want to get burned? _____

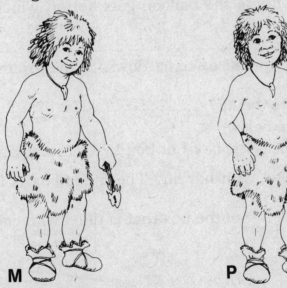

M   P

14. Fill in the blanks.

   a. Some scales weigh things that are heavy. These scales tell how

   many _____ things weigh.

   b. Some scales weigh things that are not very heavy. These scales

   tell how many _____ things weigh.

LESSON 107

A

Story items

1. Look at the picture below.
   a. Which hand will get burned, hand A or hand B? _____

   b. Which way does the heat move to reach that hand? _____

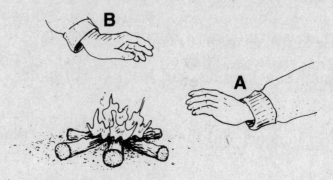

2. Which is heavier, hot air or cold air? _____
3. Let's say you are in a hot air balloon.
   a. When the air inside the balloon gets hotter, which way does the

   balloon move? _____
   b. Let's say you wanted to come down to the ground again. What

   would you do to the air? _____
4. Look at the picture below.
   a. Which box is heavier, box J or box L? _____

   b. One box is filled with hot air. The other box is filled with cold

   air. Write the letter of the box that is filled with cold air. _____

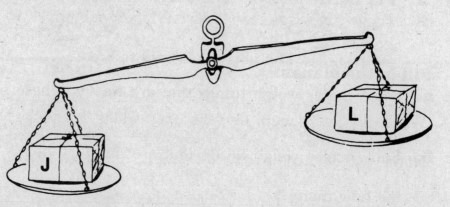

5. Will hot air in a room move **up** or **down?** _____

6. Will cold air in a room move **up** or **down?** _____

7. a. When the air in a room becomes cooler, flies like to find the warmest part of the room. Do they sit on **the floor, the walls,**

   or **the ceiling?** _____

   b. Why is that part the warmest? _____

   _____

8. Look at the picture below. There's a fire in the room, and the room is going to fill up with smoke.
   a. Write the word **first** on the part that will fill with smoke first.
   b. Write the word **second** on the part that will fill with smoke next.
   c. Write the word **last** on the part that will fill with smoke last.

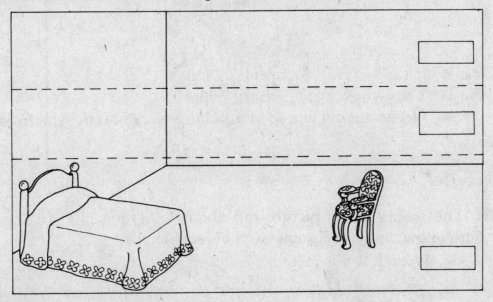

Review items

9. a. Fill in the blank. Eohippus lived _____ million years ago.
   b. Name two ways that the front leg of eohippus was different from

   the front leg of a horse that lives today. _____

   _____

10. When the horse went into the open fields, it changed in three ways.

   Name two of those ways. _____

   _____

11. Look at the picture below. It shows a pile of garbage.
  a. Write the words **earlier** and **later** in the right boxes.
  b. Which thing went into the pile earlier, thing L or thing B? _____
  c. Which thing went into the pile earlier, thing L or thing J? _____
  d. Which thing went into the pile later, thing P or thing R? _____
  e. Which thing went into the pile later, thing P or thing J? _____

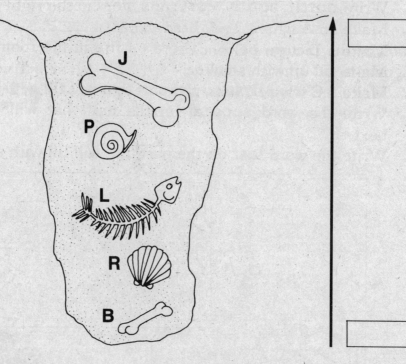

12. The scales in the picture tell about kilograms. Fill in the blanks to tell how many kilograms each object weighs.

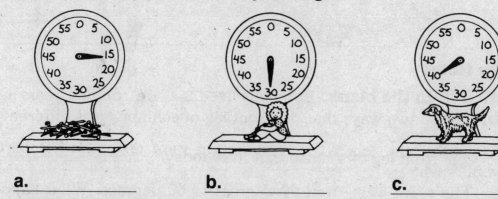

  a. _____   **b.** _____   **c.** _____

13. Look at the picture .
  a. Make a **D** on the shadow of the dog.
  b. Make an **M** on the shadow of the house.
  c. Make a **C** on the shadow of the car.
  d. Make a **T** on the shadow of the tree.

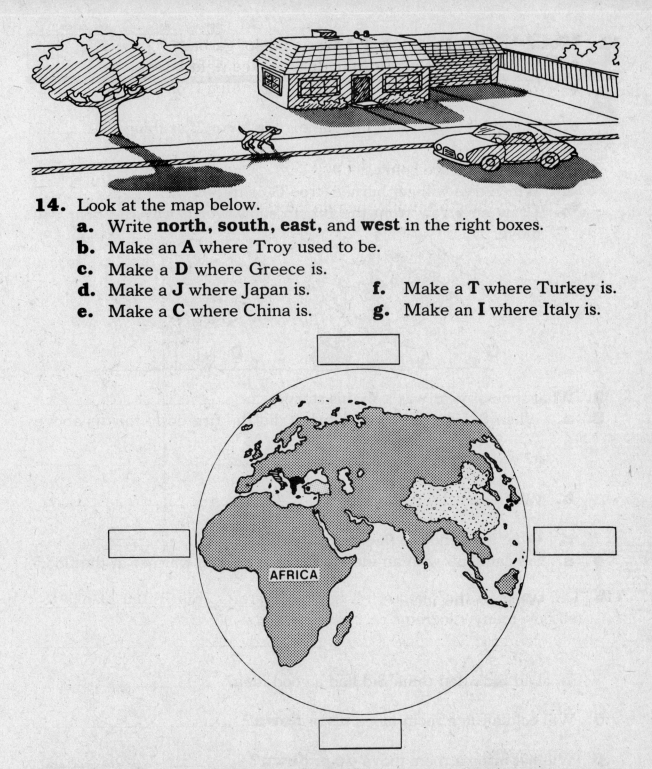

14. Look at the map below.
  a. Write **north, south, east,** and **west** in the right boxes.
  b. Make an **A** where Troy used to be.
  c. Make a **D** where Greece is.
  d. Make a **J** where Japan is.
  f. Make a **T** where Turkey is.
  e. Make a **C** where China is.
  g. Make an **I** where Italy is.

AFRICA

15. For each item, tell if the temperature went up or the temperature went down.
  a. The room went from 90 degrees to 60 degrees. What happened

  to the temperature? _____
  b. The stove went from 4 hundred degrees to 5 hundred degrees.

  What happened to the temperature? _____

LESSON 108

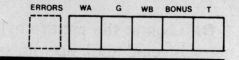

A

Story items

1. Look at the picture below.
   a. Which tree will get burned, tree G or tree D? _____
   b. Draw an arrow from the fire to show which way the heat will move.

2. What time of year was it in this story? _____

3. a. When Sid started the fire, what did the fire do to the air above

   it? _____

   b. Which way did that air move? _____

   c. What happened to the tree? _____

4. a. Sid came up with an idea to make the room warmer at the floor.

   What was his idea? _____

   _____

   b. Did Sid's dad think Sid had a good idea? _____

5. Will cold air in a room move **up** or **down?** _____

6. Will hot air in a room move **up** or **down?** _____

7. a. When the air in a room becomes cooler, flies like to find the warmest part of the room. Do they sit on **the floor, the walls,**

   or **the ceiling?** _____

   b. Why is that part the warmest? _____

   _____

8. Look at the picture below. There's a fire in the room, and the room is going to fill up with smoke.
   a. Write the word **first** on the part that will fill with smoke first.
   b. Write the word **second** on the part that will fill with smoke next.
   c. Write the word **last** on the part that will fill with smoke last.

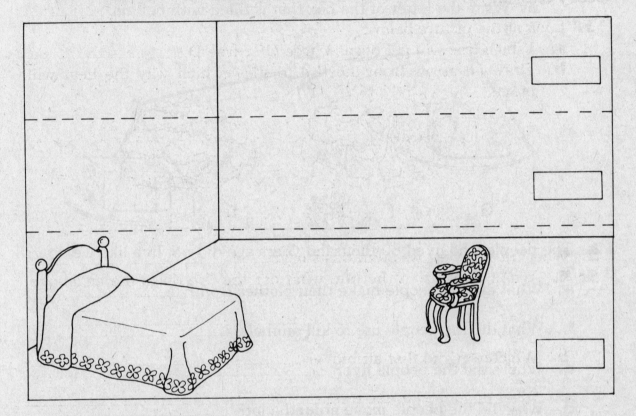

Review items

9. For each item, tell if the temperature went up or the temperature went down.
   a. The water went from 80 degrees to 20 degrees. What happened

   to the temperature? _____

   b. The rock went from 90 degrees to 80 degrees. What happened

   to the temperature? _____

10. a. Let's say you are in a hot air balloon. When the air inside the

   balloon gets hotter, which way does the balloon move? _____

   b. Let's say you wanted to come down to the ground again. What

   would you do to the air? _____

11. a. Which is lighter, hot air or cold air? _____

b. Look at the picture below. Which box is lighter, box K or box S?

_____

c. One box is filled with hot air. The other box is filled with cold air. Write the letter of the box that is filled with hot air. _____

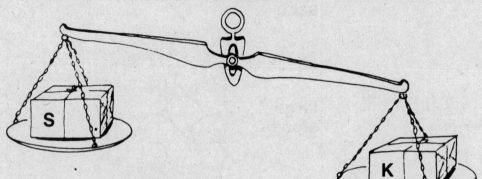

12. The people who lived 80 thousand years ago did not live like we do.

a. What did the people make their clothes from? _____

b. What did the people use to kill animals? _____

c. Where did the people live? _____

d. Why did the people move around a lot? _____

_____

13. a. What makes the sound of thunder? _____

b. Which comes first, lightning or thunder? _____

14. Look at the picture. It shows a hole dug near a beach.
a. When we dig into the pile, what's the first thing we find?

_____

b. What's the next thing we find? _____

c. What's the next thing we find? _____

d. What's the next thing we find? _____

e. What's the last thing we find? _____

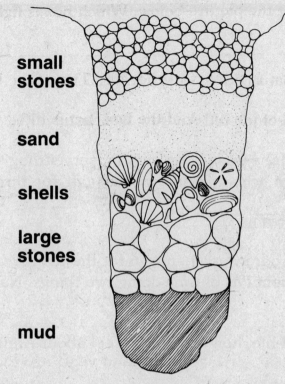

small
stones

sand

shells

large
stones

mud

15. a. What clue could tell you that somebody ate chicken?

_____

b. What clue could tell you that somebody ate coconut?

_____

LESSON 109

ERRORS	WA	G	WB	BONUS	T

A

In today's lesson, you read about filling out a bank form. Pretend you are Sid and use what you learned to fill out the form below. The facts that you need are on page 228 of your textbook.

1. Last Name _____ **2.** First Name _____

3. Street Address _____

4. City _____ **5.** State _____

6. Phone Number _____

7. How much money are you putting in the bank? $ _____

B
Story items

8. What do banks do? _____

9. What kind of job did Andrew Dexter have? _____

10. When Andrew was young, was he very strong? _____

11. a. In high school, Andrew went out for three teams. Name those

three teams. _____

b. Was Andrew good enough for the teams? _____

12. Andrew spent lots of time doing two things. Name those two things.

_____

13. a. In real life, how did people feel about Andrew?

_____

b. In Andrew's dreams, how did people feel about him?

_____

14. Look at the picture.
   a. What kind of place is in this picture? _____
   b. **Circle** each teller.
   c. Write **C** on the counter.
   d. Write **P** on the person giving money to the teller.
   e. Write **L** on the person who is leaving.

Review items

15. a. How long did the war between Troy and Greece go on? _____

    b. What did the Greek army build to help them get inside the

    wall of Troy? _____

    c. Who won the war — Troy or Greece? _____

16. a. **Fill in the blank.** Eohippus lived _____ million years ago.

    b. Name two ways that the front leg of eohippus was different from

    the front leg of a horse that lives today. _____

    _____

17. Look at the picture below. Write these names on the picture to show
where each liquid is: **crude oil, fresh water, salt water.**

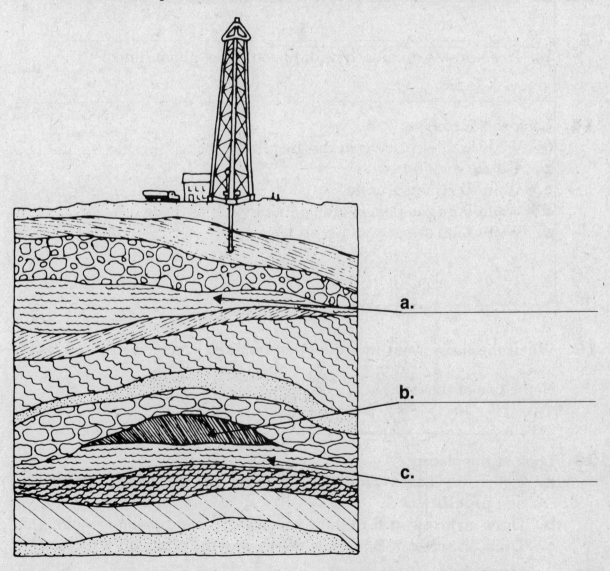

a. _____

b. _____

c. _____

18. Fill in the blanks on the time line.
   a. Write **NOW** next to the dot that shows the year now.
   b. Write **4 thousand years ago** next to the right dot.
   c. Write **1 hundred years ago** next to the right dot.
   d. Write **1 thousand years ago** next to the right dot.
   e. Write **2 thousand years ago** next to the right dot.

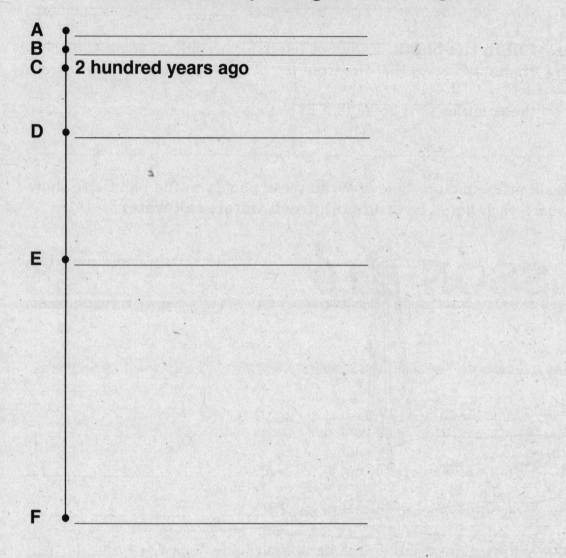

A ● _____

B ● _____

C ● **2 hundred years ago**

D ● _____

E ● _____

F ● _____

19. When the horse went into the open fields, it changed in three ways.

Name two of those ways. _____

_____

20. Look at the picture.
   a. Fill in the boxes with the names for the **refinery, crude oil,** and **pipeline.**
   b. Draw an arrow at **R** to show which way the crude oil is moving.
   c. Draw an arrow at **S** to show which way the crude oil is moving.

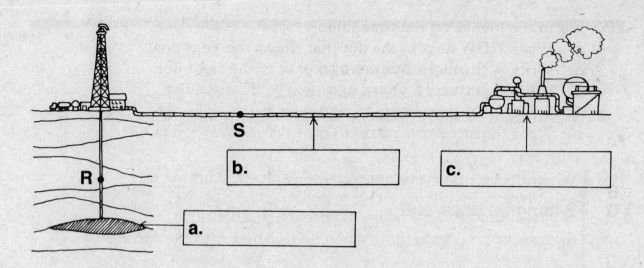

S

R

b.

c.

a.

LESSON 110

A

In today's lesson you read about checks. Use what you learned to do these items.

1. Look at the check below.

    a. When was the check written? _____

    b. Who should the bank pay? _____

    c. How much should the bank pay? _____

    d. Whose money should the bank use to pay Tom Lee? _____

May 10, 1979

Pay to _Tom Lee_ _10_ **dollars**

Ten **dollars**

Rod Mack

B

Story items

2. When Andrew said thank you to the first customer, what did the first

customer say? _____

3. When the second customer came to Andrew, Andrew was

daydreaming. What was he daydreaming about? _____

4. Andrew noticed something when he finished with the second

customer. What did he notice? _____

5. What did Mr. Franks want Andrew to do with the package?

_____

6. a. Did Andrew know what was in the package? _____

    b. If you held the package in your hand, how would it feel? _____

7. As Andrew drove to Magnetic Research Company, what was he

thinking about? _____

8. Why did a woman in a car yell at Andrew?

_____

9. What did Andrew tell himself after the woman yelled at him?

_____

Review items

10. a. How long did the war between Troy and Greece go on? _____

     b. What did the Greek army build to help them get inside the

     wall of Troy? _____

     c. Who won the war — Troy or Greece? _____

11. Look at the picture below.

    a. Fill in the boxes with the names for the **pipeline, refinery,** and **crude oil.**

    b. Draw an arrow at **A** to show which way the crude oil is moving.

    c. Draw an arrow at **B** to show which way the crude oil is moving.

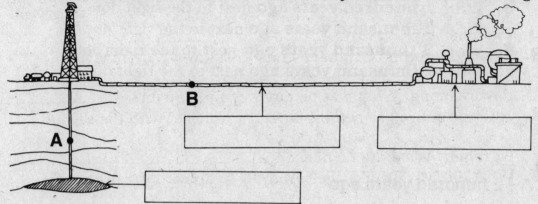

12. Here's a picture of a jet.

    a. Draw a dotted arrow from a jet engine to show which way the air will move.

    b. Draw a solid arrow on the plane to show which way it will move.

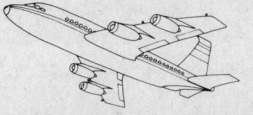

13. Look at the picture below. Write these names on the picture to show where each liquid is: **crude oil, fresh water, salt water.**

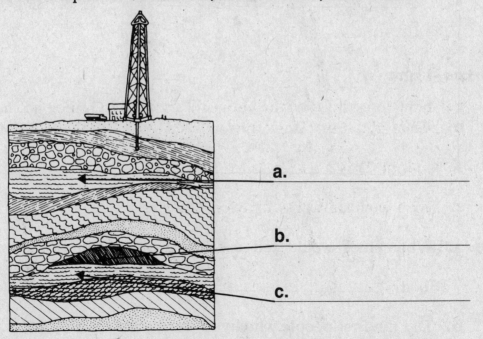

    a.

    b.

    c.

14. People who lived 80 thousand years ago did not have houses like we

have. **Finish the sentence.** Some of those people lived in _____

15. Fill in the blanks on the time line.
  a. Write **NOW** next to the dot that shows the year now.
  b. Write **1 hundred years ago** next to the right dot.
  c. Write **2 thousand years ago** next to the right dot.
  d. Write **3 thousand years ago** next to the right dot.
  e. Write **1 thousand years ago** next to the right dot.

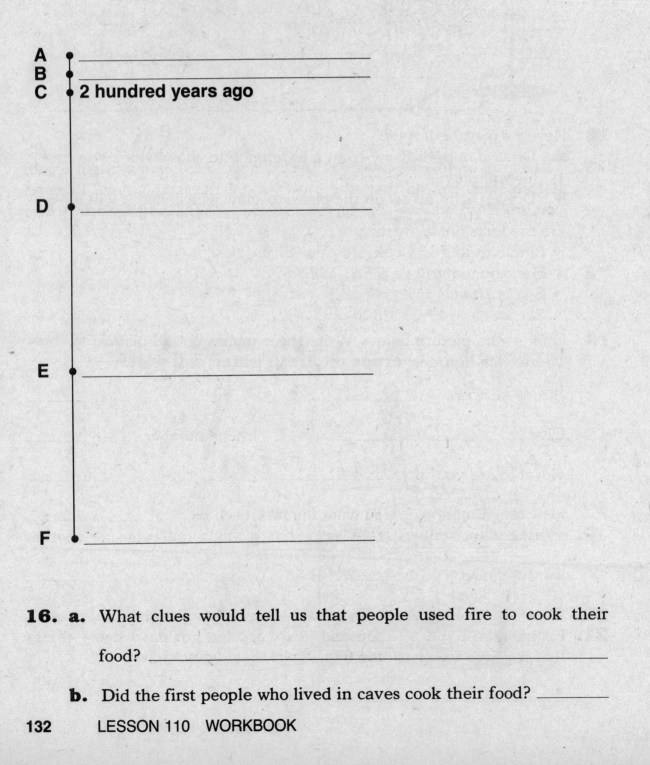

A
B
C **2 hundred years ago**

D _____

E _____

F _____

16. a. What clues would tell us that people used fire to cook their

food? _____

b. Did the first people who lived in caves cook their food? _____

c. How do we know? _____

_____

17. Look at the picture below.
　a. Which tree will get burned — tree A or tree B? _____
　b. Draw an arrow from the fire to show which way the heat will move.

A   B

18. The name of Jokey's owner is Barb Davis. Barb wants to get a job. Before Barb can do that, she must fill out the form below. Pretend you are Barb and use the facts about Barb to fill out the form. Here are the facts about Barb:
- She lives at 381 Cook Street in Chicago.
- Her phone number is 683-1121.
- She is 30 years old.
- She wants to make $800 every month.

Last name: _____ First Name: _____

Street Address: _____

City: _____ Phone number: _____

How old are you? _____

How much money do you want to make each month? _____

19. Finish the sentence. A word that sounds the same as another

word is called a _____

20. Name the tool we use to find out how much things weigh. _____

21. People who lived 80 thousand years ago did not have many things that we have today. Name four things they did not have.

_____

LESSON 111

ERRORS   WA   G   WB   BONUS   T

A

Story items

1. Name two things that a strong magnet can pick up.

_____

2. a. Electricity can turn any steel bar into a magnet. What are these

magnets called? _____

b. Name a place where these magnets are used.

_____

3. Andrew walked into a room that was filled with something. What

was it filled with? _____

4. a. What made the motor in the package run? _____

_____

b. Magnetic Research Company had a plan for motors like the one

in the package. What was that plan? _____

_____

5. When Andrew walked into the room, the motor melted and burned
his hands. What else did the motor do to Andrew?

_____

6. Did Andrew know what had happened to him? _____
7. How did Andrew's legs and arms feel when he left Magnetic

Research Company? _____

8. What happened when Andrew tugged at his car door? _____

_____

Review items

9. Look at the check below.

    a. When was the check written? _____

    b. Who should the bank pay? _____

    c. How much should the bank pay? _____

    d. Whose money should the bank use to pay Bertha Turner?

    _____

March 6, 1980

Pay to *Bertha Turner*   *6*   **dollars**

Six _____ **dollars**

Bill Capp

---

10. a. How many legs does an insect have? _____

    b. How many legs does a fly have? _____

    c. How many legs does a mosquito have? _____

    d. How many legs does a flea have? _____

    e. How many legs does a spider have? _____

    f. How many legs does an ant have? _____

    g. How many legs does a water strider have? _____

11. The picture shows a water wheel under a waterfall.
  a. Draw an arrow to show which way A will move.
  b. Start at B and draw an arrow around the shaft to show which way it will turn.
  c. Draw an arrow at C to show which way the vine will move when the shaft turns.

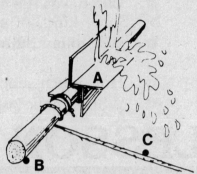

12. The dotted arrow shows which way the girl will jump. Make a solid arrow on the back of the boat to show which way it will move.

13. How does fire like to move — up or down? _____

14. a. How was the earliest horse different from horses that live today?

_____

  b. The earliest horses on earth are not alive today. How long ago

  did the earliest horses live? _____

15. Look at the picture below. Under each horse, write what kind of horse is shown.

b. _____   **c.** _____

a. _____

d. _____   **e.** _____

16. a. Cave people painted pictures of horses on cave walls. How are those horses different from horses that live today?

_____

b. Some kinds of animals that lived thousands of years ago are not alive today. How do we know what those animals looked like?

_____

LESSON 112

A

In today's lesson you read about the strength of animals. Use what you learned to do these items.

1. a. How much does a leopard weigh? _____

b. How much weight can a leopard carry? _____

2. How much weight can a large lion carry? _____

3. a. How much does a chimpanzee weigh? _____

b. How much force can a chimpanzee pull with? _____

c. How much force can a strong man pull with? _____

4. Name the strongest land animal in the world. _____

B

Story items

5. How strong is Andrew? _____

6. List two things that show how strong an elephant is. _____

_____

_____

7. How did Andrew know that Mr. Franks was mad? _____

_____

8. Andrew didn't ring the bell by the front door at Magnetic Research Company. Tell why. _____

9. Mr. Franks had a talk with Andrew when Andrew got back to the bank. What was the outcome of that talk? _____

10. a. How high did Andrew jump to catch the baseball? _____

   b. Had anybody ever jumped that high before Andrew did? _____

11. Andrew threw the ball to the catcher. How fast did that ball move?

_____

12. The catcher is going to catch three different balls. Look at the speed of the three baseballs flying through the air. One ball will knock the catcher over. One ball will knock the catcher a little bit, but it won't knock him over. One ball will do nothing.

   a. Write **knock over** next to the ball that will knock the catcher over.

   b. Make an arrow under the catcher to show which way he will fall when the ball knocks him over.

   c. Write **knock a little** next to the ball that will knock the catcher back a little.

   d. Write **nothing** next to the ball that will not knock the catcher back at all.

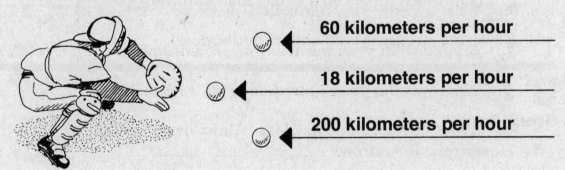

60 kilometers per hour _____

18 kilometers per hour _____

200 kilometers per hour _____

Review items

13. a. How many legs does an insect have? _____

   b. How many legs does a fly have? _____

   c. How many legs does a bird have? _____

d. How many legs does a flea have? _____

e. How many legs does a spider have? _____

f. How many legs does a water strider have? _____

g. How many legs does an ant have? _____

14. a. Name two things that a strong magnet can pick up.

_____

b. Electricity can turn any steel bar into a magnet. What are these

magnets called? _____

c. Name a place where these magnets are used.

_____

15. a. What year is it now? _____
b. How long ago did the story of Troy take place?

_____

c. In what year did the United States become a country? _____

d. What was the year 1 hundred years ago? _____

e. What was the year 3 hundred years ago? _____

f. Around what year was the first airplane made? _____

g. What was the year 2 hundred years ago? _____

h. About how long ago did Jesus Christ live?

_____

i. What year were you born in? _____

16. The picture below shows a water wheel under a waterfall.
    a. Draw an arrow to show which way A will move.
    b. Start at B and draw an arrow around the shaft to show which way it will turn.
    c. Draw an arrow at C to show which way the vine will move when the shaft turns.

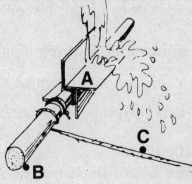

LESSON 113

ERRORS	WA	G	WB	BONUS	T

A

In today's lesson you read about football. Use what you learned to do these items.

1. The picture below shows two parts of a football player's uniform. Under each part, write what the part is.

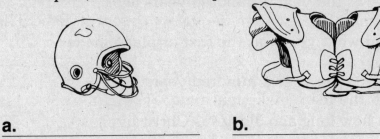

    a. _____   **b.** _____

2. How long is a football field? _____

3. Name two ways that a football team can move the ball down the

    field. _____

    _____

4. If a team moves the ball all the way to the other end of the field, that

    team gets points. How many points? _____

5. If team A has the ball, what does team B try to do? _____

_____

B

Story items

6. Andrew did two impossible things at the playground. List those two

things. _____

_____

7. Who was Denny Brock? _____

8. Denny Brock was almost always mad. Tell why. _____

_____

9. The people who owned the Titans were unhappy. What did they tell

Denny Brock they might do? _____

10. a. How many fans came to the ball park to watch most professional

teams? _____

b. How many fans came to the ball park to watch the Titans?

_____

11. Why didn't the team make much money? _____

_____

12. Why did Andrew lie to the guard? _____

_____

13. a. Did Denny want to talk to Andrew? _____

b. What was Denny going to do if Andrew didn't leave? _____

_____

Skill items

14. Here's the rule: **The more fans that come to a game, the more money the team gets from tickets.**

The list below tells how many fans come to watch each team.

a. **Circle** the name of the team that gets the most money from tickets.

b. **Underline** the name of the team that gets the least money from tickets.

- Rams .... 50 thousand fans
- Wildcats .... 60 thousand fans
- Jets .... 40 thousand fans
- Chargers .... 50 thousand fans
- Spartans .... 30 thousand fans
- Bulls .... 50 thousand fans

Review items

15. Name the strongest land animal in the world. _____

16. Look at the speed of the three baseballs flying through the air.

a. Write **knock over** next to the ball that will knock the catcher over.

b. Make an arrow under the catcher to show which way he will fall when the ball knocks him over.

c. Write **knock a little** next to the ball that will knock the catcher back a little.

d. Write **nothing** next to the ball that will not knock the catcher back at all.

220 kilometers per hour

75 kilometers per hour

20 kilometers per hour

17. List two things that show how strong an elephant is.

_____

_____

18. a. How are the legs of a racehorse different from the legs of a draft horse? _____

b. How is the back of a racehorse different from the back of a quarter horse? _____

19. a. When the air in a room becomes cooler, flies like to find the warmest part of the room. Do they sit on **the floor, the walls,** or **the ceiling?** _____

b. Why is that part the warmest? _____

_____

LESSON 114

A

In today's lesson, you read about seconds. Use what you learned to do these items.

1. Finish the sentence. A second is a unit of _____

2. Look at the stopwatches below.
 a. Which stopwatch shows that 2 seconds have passed? _____

 b. Which stopwatch shows that 6 seconds have passed? _____

 c. Which stopwatch shows that 8 seconds have passed? _____

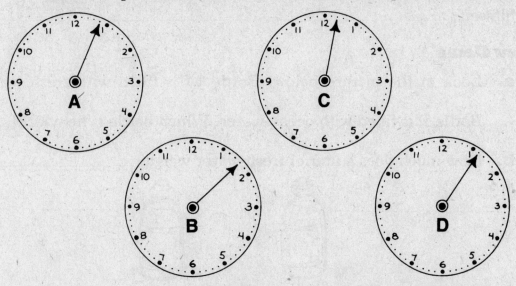

B

Story items

3. a. What happened to the best player on the Titans?

_____

b. What was that player's job on the team? _____

c. How did Denny feel about that player getting hurt? _____

4. Did Denny believe that Andrew could kick? _____

5. a. Did Andrew know what hang-time is? _____

b. Why didn't Andrew tell what hang-time is? _____

_____

6. What is hang-time? _____

_____

7. Andrew was standing on the field holding the football. Who was

watching him? _____

8. Fill in the blank. Denny told Andrew, "I want to see a

_____-second hang-time."

9. Everyone was laughing at Andrew. What did Andrew say to

himself? _____

Review items

10. a. Look at the picture below. Bottle **M** is filled with fresh water.

Bottle **P** is filled with ocean water. Which bottle is heavier? _____

b. How much does a liter of fresh water weigh? _____

M   P

11. How long is a football field? _____

12. a. Where are mosquitoes born? _____

b. Finish the sentence. When a mosquito is born, it is called a

_____

c. What do mosquitoes have to do before they can lay eggs?

_____

13. a. Name two ways that a football team can move the ball down the

field. _____

b. If a team moves the ball all the way to the other end of the field,

the team gets points. How many points? _____

14. For each contraction below, write the two words that make up the contraction.

CONTRACTION	FIRST WORD	SECOND WORD
a. we've	_____	_____
b. wasn't	_____	_____
c. can't	_____	_____
d. I'm	_____	_____

15. Look at the picture below. There's a fire in the room and the room is going to fill up with smoke.
a. Write the word **first** on the part that will fill with smoke first.
b. Write the word **second** on the part that will fill with smoke next.
c. Write the word **last** on the part that will fill with smoke last.

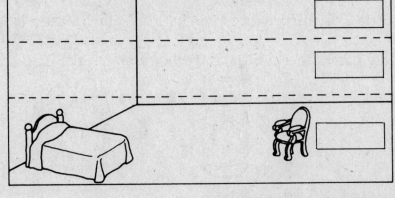

16. **a.** Let's say you are in a hot air balloon. When the air inside the balloon gets hotter, which way does the balloon move? _____

b. Let's say you wanted to come down to the ground again. What would you do to the air? _____

17. Look at picture A.

a. Write the words **earlier** and **later** in the right boxes.

b. How many years ago did layer A go into the pile? _____

c. How many years ago did layer B go into the pile? _____

d. How many years ago did layer C go into the pile? _____

e. How many years ago did layer D go into the pile? _____

f. How many years ago did layer E go into the pile? _____

18. Look at picture A. **Finish each sentence.**

a. The horse skeleton in layer A is no bigger than _____

b. The horse skeleton in layer B is about as big as _____

c. The horse skeleton in layer C is about as big as _____

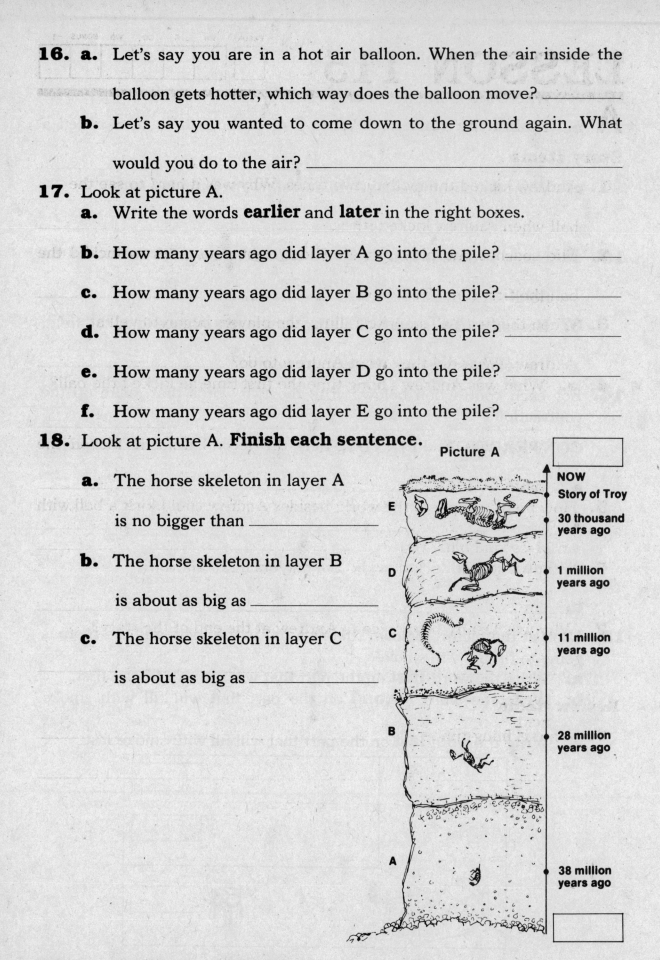

Picture A

NOW
Story of Troy
30 thousand years ago
1 million years ago
11 million years ago
28 million years ago
38 million years ago

E
D
C
B
A

LESSON 115

A

Story items

1. Andrew kicked the football two times. Why was it hard to see the

   ball when Andrew kicked it? _____

2. The coaches and players were silent right after Andrew kicked the

   ball the first time. Tell why. _____

3. When the first ball stopped rolling, the players began to yell at

   Andrew. What did they want Andrew to do? _____

4. **a.** What was Andrew's hang-time the first time he kicked the ball?

   _____

   b. What was Andrew's hang-time the second time he kicked the

   ball? _____

5. How many people in the world besides Andrew could kick a ball with

   an 11-second hang-time? _____

6. After his second kick how did the players treat Andrew?

   _____

7. Why was Denny being nice to Andrew at the end of the story?

   _____

Review items

8. What is hang-time? _____

   _____

9. Look at the stopwatches below.

    a. Which stopwatch shows that 6 seconds have passed? _____

    b. How many seconds have passed on stopwatch A? _____

    c. How many seconds have passed on stopwatch D? _____

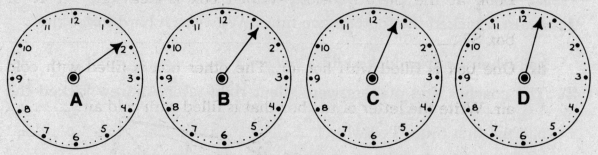

10. a. Look at the picture below. Bottle J is filled with fresh water.

       Bottle K is filled with ocean water. Which bottle is heavier? _____

    b. How much does a liter of fresh water weigh? _____

11. a. Where are mosquitoes born? _____

    b. **Finish the sentence.** When a mosquito is born it is called a

    _____

    c. What do mosquitoes have to do before they can lay eggs?

    _____

12. Finish the sentence. A second is a unit of _____

13. For each contraction below, write the two words that make up the contraction.

    CONTRACTION   FIRST WORD   SECOND WORD

    a. she'll   _____   _____

    b. I'm   _____   _____

    c. aren't   _____   _____

14. a. Will hot air in a room move **up** or **down**? _____

b. Will cold air in a room move **up** or **down**? _____

15. a. Which is heavier — hot air or cold air? _____

b. Look at the picture below. Which box is heavier, box R or

box S? _____

c. One box is filled with hot air. The other box is filled with cold

air. Write the letter of the box that is filled with cold air. _____

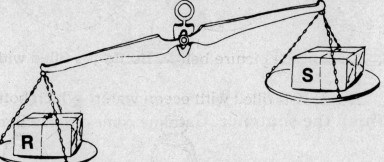

16. a. The people who lived in caves drew pictures on the cave walls.

Name three things they made pictures of. _____

_____

b. Name three things that cave people used to make paint.

_____

17. Finish each part of the rule.
a. Things near the bottom of the pile _____

_____

b. Things near the top of the pile _____

_____

18. Write a homonym for each word below.

a. new _____   **d.** to _____

b. road _____   **e.** their _____

c. eight _____

19. a. What clue could tell you that somebody ate chicken?

_____

b. What clue could tell you that somebody ate coconut?

_____

20. The scales in the picture tell about grams. Fill in the blanks to tell how many grams each object weighs.

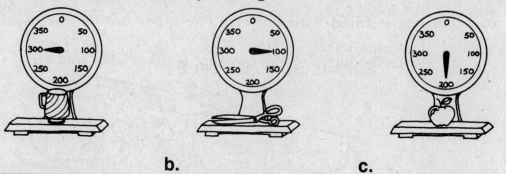

a. _____ **b.** _____ **c.** _____

21. Finish the sentence. Gasoline comes from a liquid called

_____

22. Look at the picture below.
   a. Make a **C** on the shadow of the dog.
   b. Make a **J** on the shadow of the house.
   c. Make a **D** on the shadow of the car.
   d. Make an **I** on the shadow of the tree.

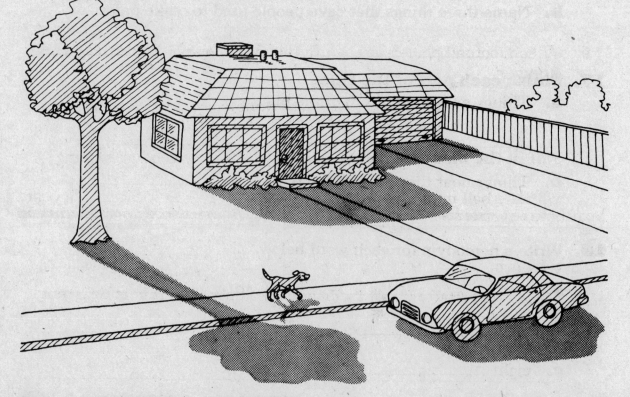

23. Look at the picture below.

a. What is the name of the vehicle in the picture? _____

b. How many wheels does the vehicle have? _____

c. What is pulling the vehicle? _____

d. What is soldier J doing? _____

e. What is soldier P doing? _____

Soldier J   **Soldier P**

LESSON 116

ERRORS	WA	G	WB	BONUS	T

A

In today's lesson you read about professional football players. Use what you learned to do these items.

1. Who makes more money, a professional football player or a bank

teller? _____

2. Which football players are worth the most money? **Underline the answer.**
- the worst players
- the players that fans want to see
- the fattest players

3. Fill in the blank. A football player who is very good at running

with the ball may earn _____ a year.

B
Story items

4. Denny told Andrew that kicking in an empty field is a lot different

from kicking in a game. How is it different? _____

5. When Andrew said that he would play for the Titans, Denny didn't jump up and down with joy. What did Denny think Andrew was

trying to do? _____

6. a. When Denny wants a player for the Titans, he makes an offer to

the player. Does the player usually take that offer? _____

b. So Denny makes a new offer. How is this offer different from the

first offer? _____

7. Denny knew that if Andrew was on the team, fans would come to the games even if the Titans lost. Why would they come?

_____

_____

8. How much was Andrew worth for each game that he played? **Circle the answer.**

- 20 thousand dollars   • 100 thousand dollars   • 50 dollars

9. a. How much money did Andrew ask for? _____

b. How much money per month did Denny say he would pay

Andrew? _____

c. How much money is that per year? **Cross out the answer.**

- 10 thousand dollars   • 120 dollars   • 120 thousand dollars

10. After the men shook hands, both men were happy.

a. Why was Denny happy? _____

_____

b. Why was Andrew happy? _____

_____

Review items

11. Look at the picture below.

a. Which tree will get burned — tree A or tree B? _____

b. Draw an arrow from the fire to show which way the heat will move.

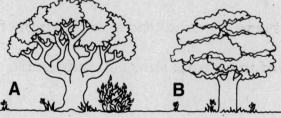

12. a. Fill in the blank. If something weighs one kilogram, it weighs

_____ grams.

b. Fill in the blank. If something weighs four kilograms, it weighs

_____ grams.

13. Write two words that sound the same but are not spelled the same.

Be sure to spell the words correctly. _____

14. Look at the picture.
   a. Write **north, south, east,** and **west** in the right boxes.

   b. Which animal is facing into the wind? _____

   c. Which direction is that animal facing? _____

   d. So what's the name of the wind? _____

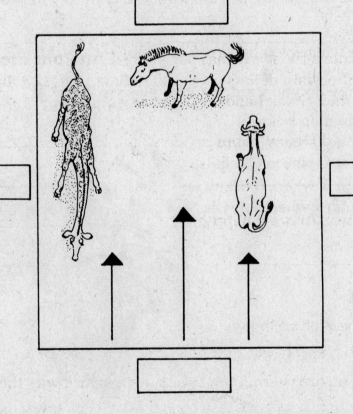

15. When the horse went into the open fields, it changed in three ways.

Name two of those ways. _____

16. Mr. Daniels wants to get a new job. Before Mr. Daniels can do that, he must fill out the form below. Pretend you are Mr. Daniels and use the facts about Mr. Daniels to fill out the form. Here are the facts about Mr. Daniels.

- His name is John Daniels.
- His address is 1436 Field Street, San Francisco, California.
- His phone number is 621-0664.
- He used to work at Reef Oil Company.
- He wants to make two thousand dollars every month.
- He is 40 years old.

Last Name: _____ First Name: _____

Street Address: _____

City: _____ State: _____

What is your phone number? _____

How old are you? _____

Name the place where you had your last job: _____

How much money do you want to make every month? $ _____

17. Look at the map below.
  a. Make a **J** where Japan is.
  b. Make a **C** where China is.
  c. Make a **T** where Turkey is.
  d. Make an **I** where Italy is.

AFRICA

18. a. Name three relatives of the word **run.** _____

  b. Name three relatives of the word **jump.** _____

LESSON 117

A
Story items

1. Before Andrew's first game, announcements appeared in the newspapers.
   a. What impression did the announcements give? _____

   _____

   b. Did the announcements tell what Andrew could do? _____
   c. Why did the Titans place those announcements in the paper?

   _____

2. a. How many fans came to Andrew's first game? _____

   b. Who were the fans talking about? _____

   c. Why didn't the fans think the Titans would win? _____

   _____

3. a. How did the players feel just before the game started? _____

   b. Why was Andrew more frightened than the other players?

   _____

   _____

4. a. Who kicked the ball at the beginning of the game? _____

   b. Who caught the ball? _____

   c. How far was the ball from the goal line? _____

5. How many plays did the Titans need to score their first touchdown?

   _____

6. The Wildcats got the ball. Tell two ways they moved the ball down

   the field. _____

7. How did the Titans get the ball back?

_____

8. What did the crowd do when the Titans began to lose meters?

_____

9. Why didn't the crowd laugh when they heard that Andrew was going

to kick an 80-meter field goal? _____

_____

Review items

10. Look at the picture.
   a. Write **north, south, east,** and
      west in the right boxes.
   b. Which animal is facing into

      the wind? _____
   c. Which direction is that animal

      facing? _____
   d. So what's the name of the

      wind? _____

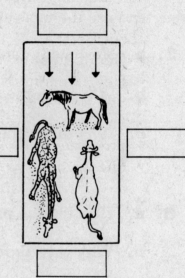

11. Look at the map.
   a. Make a **P** where Japan is.
   b. Make a **D** where China is.
   c. Make a **K** where Turkey is.
   d. Make an **L** where Italy is.

AFRICA

12. a. Fill in the blank. If something weighs one kilogram, it weighs

_____ grams.

b. Fill in the blank. If something weighs seven kilograms, it

weighs _____ grams.

13. When the horse went into the open fields, it changed in three ways.

Name two of those ways. _____

_____

14. Bertha Turner wants to put some money in the bank. Before she can
do that, she must fill out the form below. Pretend you are Bertha
and use the facts about her to fill out the form. Here are the facts
about Bertha.
- Her address is 953 Park Lane, San Francisco, California.
- Her phone number is 663-0100.
- She works as a special consultant.
- Her boss is Bonnie Sanchez.
- She makes two hundred dollars every day that she works.
- She wants to put three hundred dollars in the bank.

First Name: _____ Last Name: _____

Street Address: _____

City: _____ State: _____

Who is your boss? _____

What is your job? _____

How much money do you make every day that you work? _____

How much money do you want to put in the bank? _____

15. a. Fill in the blank. Eohippus lived _____ million years ago.

b. Name two ways that the front leg of eohippus was different from

the front leg of a horse that lives today. _____

_____

LESSON 118

A

Story items

1. a. How far did Andrew kick the ball? _____

   b. Why wasn't it a field goal? _____

_____

2. The Wildcats were winning, and the Titans were getting hurt.

   a. Name the player who was hurting the Titans. _____

   b. Name two things that tell what Smiling Sam looked like. _____

_____

3. a. The coach didn't want Andrew to talk to Smiling Sam. Tell why.

_____

   b. Andrew talked to Smiling Sam anyway. Did Andrew scare Smiling Sam?

_____

4. When the ball came to Andrew, he waited for somebody. Who?

_____

5. List three things that happened to Smiling Sam when Andrew hit him.
   ① _____

   ② _____

   ③ _____

6. Why were the Titans surprised when Andrew ran with the ball?

_____

7. a. Fill in the blank. In the game with the Wildcats, Andrew

scored _____ touchdowns.

   b. Which team won the game? _____

8. Some of Andrew's hang-times are shown on the stopwatches.

   a. **Circle** the watch that shows his best hang-time.

   b. **Underline** the watch that shows his worst hang-time.

   c. How many seconds are shown on the watch that you circled? _____

   d. How many seconds are shown on the watch that you underlined?

_____

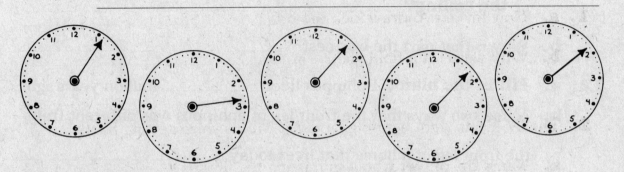

Review items

9. **a.** What is the temperature inside your body when you are

   healthy? _____

   b. **Fill in the blank.** Most fevers don't go over _____ degrees.

   c. Name two things that may happen when people have very high

   fevers. _____

   _____

10. **a.** What year is it now? _____

   b. What year were you born in? _____

   c. Around what year was the first airplane made? _____

   d. What was the year 1 hundred years ago? _____

   e. What was the year 2 hundred years ago? _____

   f. In what year did the United States become a country? _____

   g. What was the year 3 hundred years ago? _____

   h. About how long ago did Jesus Christ live?

   _____

i. How long ago did the story of Troy take place?

_____

11. a. When the air in a room becomes cooler, flies like to find the warmest part of the room. Do they sit on **the floor, the walls,**

or **the ceiling?** _____

b. Why is that part the warmest? _____

12. a. **Fill in the blank.** Eohippus lived _____ million years ago.

b. Name two ways that the front leg of eohippus was different from

the front leg of a horse that lives today. _____

_____

13. Look at the check below.
a. When was the check written? _____

b. Who should the bank pay? _____

c. How much should the bank pay? _____

d. Whose money should the bank use to pay Liz Rich? _____

June 3, 1979

Pay to _____Liz Rich_____ __12__ dollars

_____Twelve_____ dollars

_____Alice Kapp_____

---

14. a. How long is a football field? _____

b. Name two ways that a football team can move the ball down the

field. _____

c. What is it called when the team reaches the other end of the field? _____

d. If a team moves the ball all the way to the other end of the field, the team gets points. How many points? _____

15. a. What makes the sound of thunder? _____

b. Which comes first, lightning or thunder? _____

LESSON 119

ERRORS	WA	G	WB	BONUS	T

A
Story items

1. The newspapers made up a name for Andrew. What name?

_____

2. Why didn't Andrew daydream anymore?

_____

3. Everything changed when Andrew started playing with the Titans.

a. How did the players change? _____

_____

b. How did the coaches change? _____

_____

c. How did the owners of the team change? _____

_____

4. When Andrew ran with the ball, nobody could stop him. How did it feel to run into Andrew? _____

5. Finish the sentence. On the sixth Sunday, Andrew felt strange. When he was getting dressed for the game, he noticed that his

hands and feet _____

6. Andrew used to be as strong as an African elephant.

    a. How strong was he now? _____

    b. How did Andrew feel when he realized he was losing his

        strength? _____

Review items

  7. a. What year is it now? _____

    b. What was the year 1 hundred years ago? _____

    c. Around what year was the first airplane made? _____

    d. What year were you born in? _____

    e. What was the year 2 hundred years ago? _____

    f. About how long ago did Jesus Christ live?

    _____

    g. What was the year 3 hundred years ago? _____

    h. In what year did the United States become a country? _____
    i. How long ago did the story of Troy take place?

    _____

  8. The picture shows a water wheel under a waterfall.

    a. Draw an arrow to show which way A will move.

    b. Start at B and draw a circular arrow
        around the shaft to show which way
        it will turn.

    c. Draw an arrow at C to
        show which way the vine
        will move when the
        shaft turns.

9. a. What is the temperature inside your body when you are

healthy? _____

b. Fill in the blank. Most fevers don't go over _____ degrees.

c. Name two things that may happen when people have very high

fevers. _____

_____

10. Look at the picture below. Write these names in the blanks to show where each liquid is: **crude oil, salt water, fresh water.**

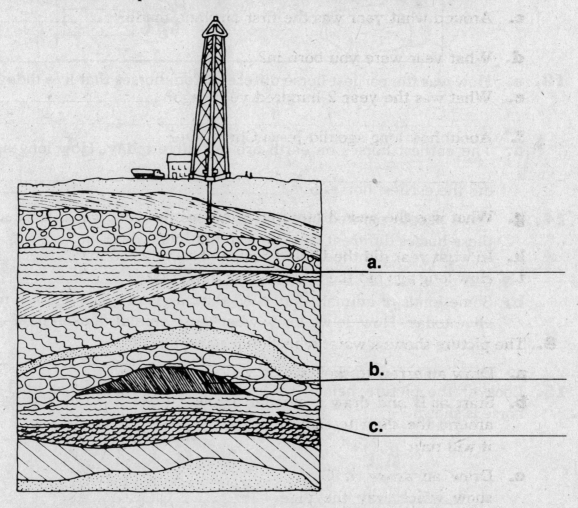

a. _____

b. _____

c. _____

11. a. How long did the war between Troy and Greece go on? _____

b. What did the Greek army build to help them get inside the

wall of Troy? _____

c. Who won the war — Troy or Greece? _____

12. Look at the picture below. There's a fire in the room and the room is going to fill up with smoke.

    a. Write the word **first** on the part that will fill with smoke first.

    b. Write the word **second** on the part that will fill up with smoke next.

    c. Write the word **last** on the part that will fill with smoke last.

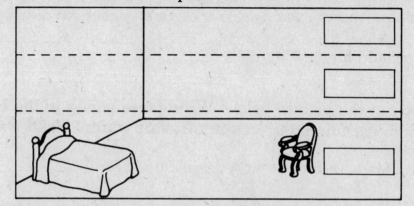

13. a. How was the earliest horse different from horses that live today?

_____

    b. The earliest horses on earth are not alive today. How long ago

did the earliest horses live? _____

14. a. Cave people painted pictures of horses on cave walls. How are those horses different from horses that live today?

_____

    b. Some kinds of animals that lived thousands of years ago are not alive today. How do we know what those animals looked like?

_____

15. Look at the picture below. Under each horse, write what kind of horse is shown.

a. _____   b. _____

c. _____ d. _____ e. _____

LESSON 120

A

Story items

1. When Andrew was as strong as an elephant, he didn't play as hard as he could have. Why not? _____

_____

2. Andrew was tackled in the first game he played after his strength faded.
   a. Had Andrew ever been tackled before? _____

   b. How many times did Andrew get tackled in that game? _____

3. How many touchdowns did Andrew make? _____

4. Did Mean George think that Andrew did a **good job** or a **bad job** in the game? _____

5. a. When the game was over, Andrew sat in the locker room. How did his arms and legs feel? _____

   b. What was happening to him? _____

   _____

6. Andrew imagined what the fans would do when he lost all his strength. Name two things Andrew thought the fans would do.

_____

7. The Titans were different during the practices. Name two ways they were different. _____

_____

8. How strong was Andrew at the end of the story?

_____

9. Andrew was getting weaker.
- **a.** **Cross out** the stopwatch that shows his hang-time when he was weakest.
- **b.** **Circle** the stopwatch that shows the best hang-time.
- **c.** How many seconds are shown on the stopwatch that you crossed out? _____
- **d.** How many seconds are shown on the stopwatch that you circled?

_____

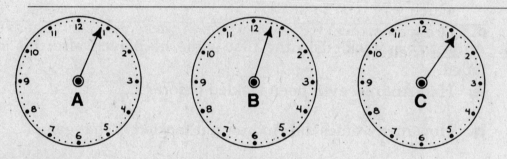

Review items

10. Fill in the blanks on the time line below.
- **a.** Write **NOW** next to the dot that shows the year now.
- **b.** Write **1 thousand years ago** next to the right dot.
- **c.** Write **1 hundred years ago** next to the right dot.
- **d.** Write **4 thousand years ago** next to the right dot.
- **e.** Write **2 hundred years ago** next to the right dot.

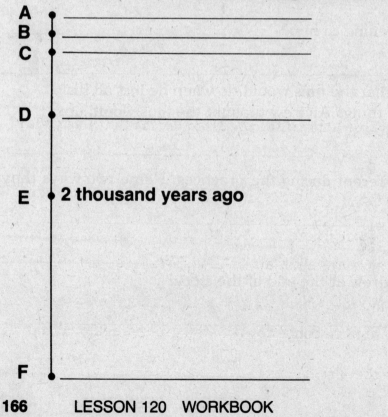

11. a. How long did the war between Troy and Greece go on? _____

b. What did the Greek army build to help them get inside the

wall of Troy? _____

c. Who won the war — Troy or Greece? _____

12. The picture shows a water wheel under a waterfall.
   a. Draw an arrow to show which way A will move.
   b. Start at B and draw a circular arrow around the shaft to show which way it will move.
   c. Draw an arrow at C to show which way the vine will move when the shaft turns.

13. a. How was the earliest horse different from horses that live today?

   _____

b. The earliest horses on earth are not alive today. How long ago

   did the earliest horses live? _____

14. a. Let's say that you are in a hot air balloon. When the air inside

   the balloon gets hotter, which way does the balloon move? _____

b. Let's say you wanted to come down to the ground again. What

   would you do to the air? _____

15. Look at the pictures below. Which picture shows how you should

hold a burning branch if you don't want to get burned? _____

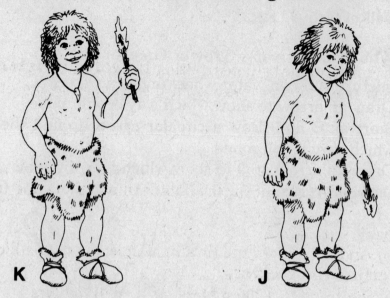

K   J

16. a. Cave people painted pictures of horses on cave walls. How are those horses different from horses that live today?

_____

b. Some kinds of animals that lived thousands of years ago are not alive today. How do we know what those animals looked like?

_____

17. Look at the picture below. Under each horse, write what kind of horse is shown.

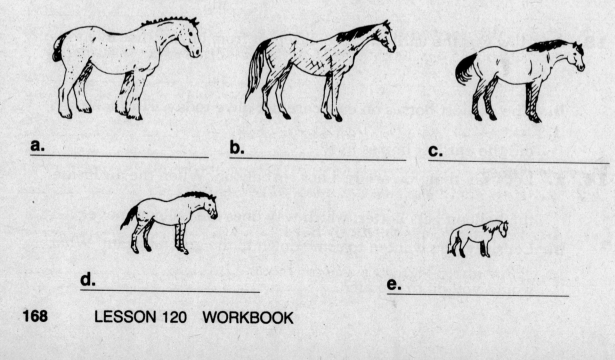

a. _____   b. _____   c. _____

d. _____   e. _____

LESSON 121

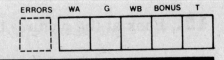
A

Story items

1. Were Andrew's hang-times getting **longer** or **shorter?** _____

2. Andrew tried to stay away from the players on the other team. Tell

   why. _____

   _____

3. It was very important for the Titans to win the game in today's story.

   Tell why. _____

4. When Andrew kicked the field goal, how far did he kick it?
   Underline the answer.
   - 90 meters
   - 50 meters
   - 40 meters
   - 60 meters

5. How did the Titans feel after the game? _____

6. How long was it before the championship game? _____

7. Andrew squeezed the handle of his locker.

   a. What was he trying to find out? _____

   b. What happened when he squeezed it? _____

8. What did Andrew want for the team? _____

   _____

9. **Finish the sentences.**

   a. When Andrew first played with the Titans, he was as strong as

   _____

   b. In today's story, Andrew was as strong as _____

Review items

10. **a.** How many legs does an insect have? _____

    b. How many legs does a fly have? _____

    c. How many legs does a horse have? _____

d. How many legs does a water strider have? _____

   e. How many legs does an ant have? _____

   f. How many legs does a flea have? _____

   g. How many legs does a spider have? _____

11. a. Let's say you are in a hot air balloon. When the air inside the balloon gets hotter, which way does the balloon move? _____

   b. Let's say you wanted to come down to the ground again. What would you do to the air? _____

12. a. Name two things that a strong magnet can pick up. _____

   b. Electricity can turn any steel bar into a magnet. What are these magnets called? _____

   c. Name a place where these magnets are used. _____

   _____

13. What is hang-time? _____

   _____

14. Look at the stopwatches below.
   a. Which stopwatch shows that six seconds have passed? _____

   b. How many seconds have passed on stopwatch C? _____

   c. How many seconds have passed on stopwatch A? _____

15. Look at the picture below.

    a. Which hand will get burned — hand F or hand K? _____

    b. Which way does the heat move to reach that hand? _____

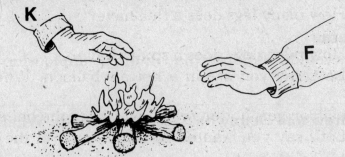

16. Look at the picture below.

    a. Fill in the boxes with the names for the **crude oil, pipeline,** and **refinery.**

    b. Draw an arrow at M to show which way the crude oil is moving.

    c. Draw an arrow at P to show which way the crude oil is moving.

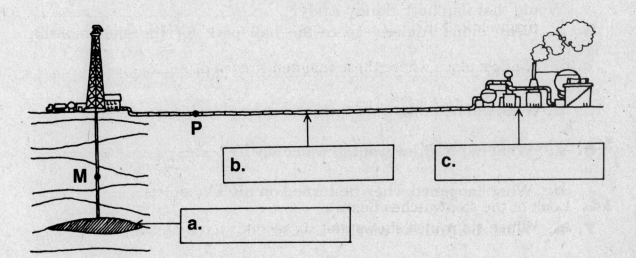

17. The people who lived 80 thousand years ago did not live like we do.

    a. What did the people make their clothes from? _____

    b. What did the people use to kill animals? _____

    c. Where did the people live? _____

    d. Why did the people move around a lot? _____

_____

LESSON 122

ERRORS WA G WB BONUS T

A

Story items

1. Why couldn't Andrew play in the championship game? _____

_____

2. Andrew told Denny he'd lost his strength. What did Denny tell

Andrew to do? _____

3. When Andrew went to the locker room, who followed him? _____

_____

4. When Mean George slapped Andrew on the back, it hurt Andrew.

Would that slap hurt Handy Andy? _____

5. a. Why didn't Andrew go to the ball park for the championship

game? _____

b. Who did he think would win the championship game? _____

6. a. What did Andrew want to watch on TV? _____

b. What happened when he turned on his TV set? _____

7. a. What did Andrew wiggle? _____

b. What was wrong with the electric cord? _____

c. What happened when Andrew wiggled the plug? _____

_____

8. How did the shock make Andrew's feet and legs feel? _____

Review items

9. Finish the sentence. A word that sounds the same as another

word is called a _____

LESSON 122 WORKBOOK

10. Look at the picture below.
  a. Fill in the names for the **crude oil, refinery,** and **pipeline.**
  b. Draw an arrow at M to show which way the crude oil is moving.
  c. Draw an arrow at T to show which way the crude oil is moving.

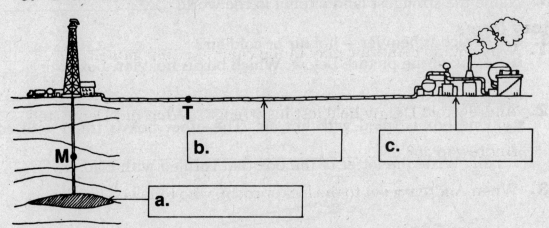

11. a. Name two things that a strong magnet can pick up. _____

_____

  b. Electricity can turn any steel bar into a magnet. What are those

magnets called? _____

  c. Name a place where these magnets are used. _____

_____

12. Finish the sentence. A second is a unit of _____
13. Look at the speed of the three baseballs flying through the air.
  a. Write **knock over** next to the ball that will knock the catcher over.
  b. Make an arrow under the catcher to show which way he will fall when the ball knocks him over.
  c. Write **knock a little** next to the ball that will knock the catcher back a little.
  d. Write **nothing** next to the ball that will not knock the catcher back at all.

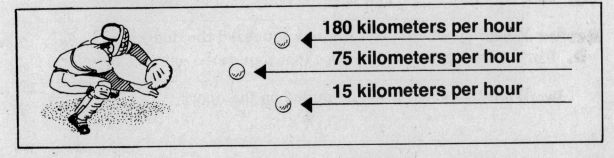

180 kilometers per hour

75 kilometers per hour

15 kilometers per hour

14. List two things that show how strong an elephant is. _____

_____

15. Name the strongest land animal in the world. _____

16. a. Which is heavier — hot air or cold air? _____

b. Look at the picture below. Which box is heavier, box **X** or

box **Y**? _____

c. One box is filled with hot air. The other box is filled with cold

air. Write the letter of the box that is filled with cold air. _____

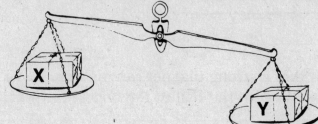

17. a. Will hot air in a room move **up** or **down**? _____

b. Will cold air in a room move **up** or **down**? _____

LESSON 123

ERRORS	WA	G	WB	BONUS	T

A

Story items

1. How did Andrew get an electric shock? _____

_____

2. The electric shock changed Andrew. How did it change him?

_____

3. a. Andrew squeezed the doorknob. What was he trying to find

out? _____

b. What happened when Andrew squeezed the doorknob?

_____

c. What happened when he pulled on the door?

_____

4. How strong was Andrew now?

_____

5. Why did Andrew run to the ball park instead of going in a car?

_____

6. As Andrew ran to the ball park, did many people recognize him?

_____

7. When Andrew got to the locker room, the game had already started.

Which team was winning? _____

8. What did the fans do when they saw Andrew? _____

9. Andrew had a plan to fool the Wildcats.

a. What was that plan? _____
b. What did Andrew do with the ball at the end of the story?

_____

Review items

10. For each contraction below, write the two words that make up the contraction.

CONTRACTION	FIRST WORD	SECOND WORD
a. we've	_____	_____
b. can't	_____	_____
c. I'll	_____	_____

11. How does fire like to move — **up** or **down**? _____

12. a. What clues would tell us that people used fire to cook their

food? _____

b. Did the first people who lived in caves cook their food? _____

c. How do we know? _____

13. Finish each part of the rule.

a. Things near the bottom of the pile _____

_____

b. Things near the top of the pile _____

_____

14. a. The people who lived in caves drew pictures on the cave walls. Name three things they made pictures of.

_____

b. Name three things that cave people used to make paint.

_____

15. Name the tool we use to find out how much things weigh. _____

16. Look at the picture below. It shows a hole dug near a beach.
a. When we dig into the pile, what's the first thing we find?

_____

b. What's the next thing we find? _____

c. What's the next thing we find? _____

d. What's the next thing we find? _____

e. What's the last thing we find? _____

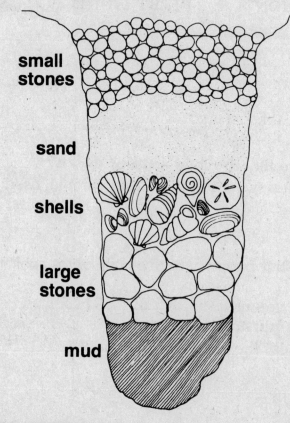

small
stones

sand

shells

large
stones

mud

17. Look at picture 1. **Finish each sentence.**

    a. The horse skeleton in layer A is no bigger than _____

    b. The horse skeleton in layer B is about as big as _____

    c. The horse skeleton in layer C is about as big as _____

18. Look at picture 1.

    a. Write the words **earlier** and **later** in the right boxes.

    b. How many years ago did layer A go into the pile? _____

    c. How many years ago did layer B go into the pile? _____

    d. How many years ago did layer C go into the pile? _____

    e. How many years ago did layer D go into the pile? _____

    f. How many years ago did layer E go into the pile? _____

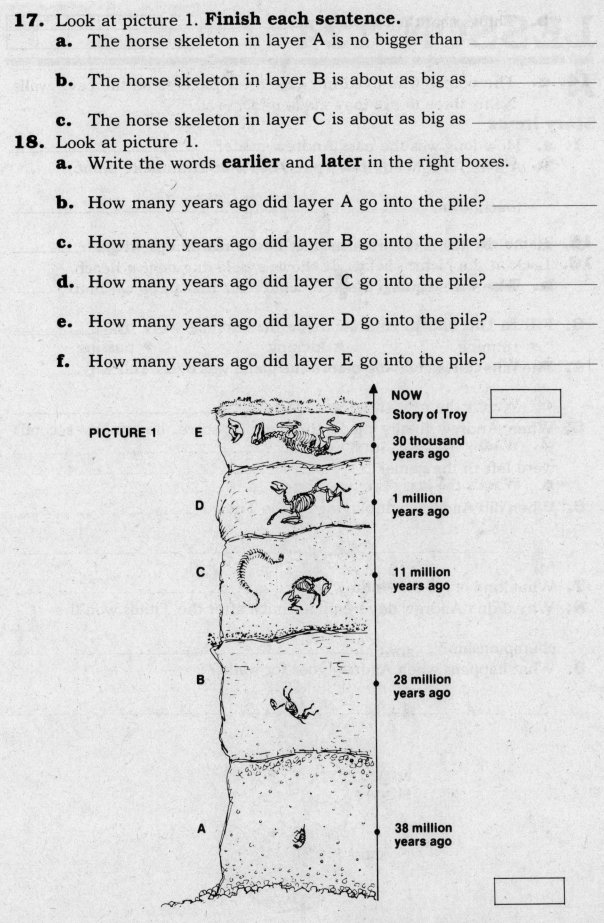

PICTURE 1

E — NOW / Story of Troy

30 thousand years ago

D — 1 million years ago

C — 11 million years ago

B — 28 million years ago

A — 38 million years ago

LESSON 124

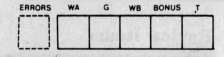

A

Story items

1. **a.** How long was the pass Andrew made? _____
   b. A Titan caught Andrew's pass. Did that Titan score a

   touchdown? _____

2. **a.** What was the score after the Titans scored a field goal? _____

   b. Who was winning? _____

3. **Fill in the blank.** Andrew made the winning score by _____
   • running   • kicking   • passing

4. The fans started leaving before the game was over. Tell why.

   _____

5. When Andrew finally made the winning score, how many seconds

   were left in the game? _____

6. When did Andrew quit playing for the Titans? _____

   _____

7. What kind of job did Andrew get? _____

8. Why didn't Andrew daydream as much after the Titans won the

   championship? _____

9. What happens when Andrew goes for walks?

   _____

Review items

10. For each contraction below, write the two words that make up the contraction.

CONTRACTION	FIRST WORD	SECOND WORD
a. you'll	_____	_____
b. I've	_____	_____
c. wouldn't	_____	_____

11. Look at the picture below. Bottle K is filled with ocean water. Bottle L is filled with fresh water.

a. Which bottle is heavier? _____

b. How much does a liter of fresh water weigh? _____

12. a. Where are mosquitoes born? _____

b. Fill in the blank. When a mosquito is born, it is called a _____

c. What do mosquitoes have to do before they can lay eggs?

_____

13. Look at the picture below. Under each horse, write what kind of horse is shown.

a. _____ **b.** _____ **c.** _____

 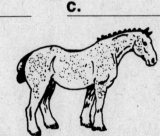

d. _____ **e.** _____

14. a. How are the legs of a racehorse different from the legs of a

draft horse? _____

b. How is the back of a racehorse different from the back of a

quarter horse? _____

15. Look at picture 1.

   a. Write the words **earlier** and **later** in the right boxes.

   b. How many years ago did layer A go into the pile? _____

   c. How many years ago did layer B go into the pile? _____

   d. How many years ago did layer C go into the pile? _____

   e. How many years ago did layer D go into the pile? _____

   f. How many years ago did layer E go into the pile? _____

16. Look at picture 1. **Finish each sentence.**

   a. The horse skeleton in layer A is no bigger

      than _____

   b. The horse skeleton in layer B is about as

      big as _____

   c. The horse skeleton in layer C is about as big

      as _____

PICTURE 1

NOW
Story of Troy

E   30 thousand years ago

D   1 million years ago

C   11 million years ago

B   28 million years ago

A   38 million years ago

17. a. What makes the sound of thunder? _____

   b. Which comes first, **thunder** or **lightning?** _____

18. Look at the picture below. It shows a pile of garbage.
   a. Write the words **earlier** and **later** in the right boxes.

   b. Which thing went into the pile earlier, thing R or thing M? _____

   c. Which thing went into the pile earlier, thing A or thing B? _____

   d. Which thing went into the pile later, thing S or thing B? _____

   e. Which thing went into the pile later, thing S or thing M? _____

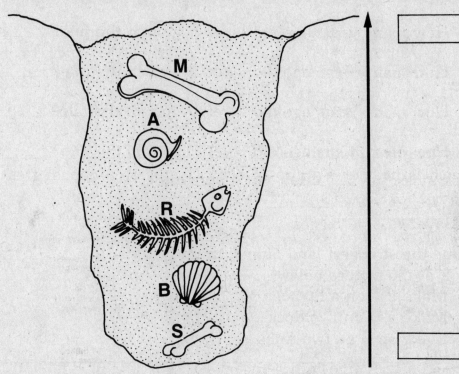

LESSON 125

A

Story items

1. a. What city did Liz Jackson live near? _____

   b. Name the ocean that is next to that city. _____
2. a. Name three kinds of horses that live today.

   _____

   b. What kind of horses did Liz Jackson raise? _____

3. a. What country did Ree come from? _____

   b. In which direction did Ree travel to get to San Francisco? _____

Review items

4. Look at the stopwatches below.

   a. How many seconds have passed on stopwatch A? _____

   b. How many seconds have passed on stopwatch B? _____

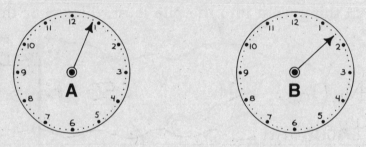

5. How long is a football field? _____

6. Which is heavier — a cup of ocean water or a cup of fresh water?

_____

7. Name the strongest land animal in the world. _____

8. Look at the picture below.

   a. Make a **T** on a tugboat.

   b. Make a **D** on two docks.

   c. Make an **S** on two ships.

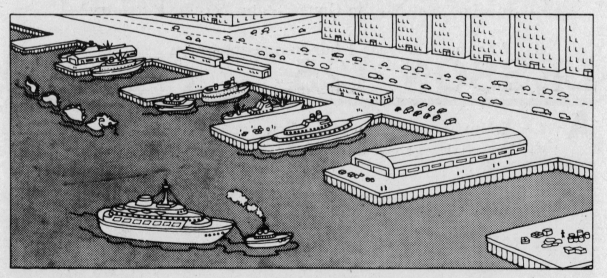

9. Electricity can turn any steel bar into a magnet. What are these

magnets called? _____

10. Look at the check below.

   a. When was the check written? _____

   b. Who should the bank pay? _____

   c. How much should the bank pay? _____

   d. Whose money should the bank use to pay Mr. Ono? _____

May 21, 1980

Pay to _Mr. Ono_   _50 thousand_ **dollars**

Fifty thousand ⌇⌇⌇⌇⌇⌇⌇⌇⌇ **dollars**

Liz Jackson

---

11. a. What year is it now? _____

   b. What year were you born in? _____

   c. In what year did the United States become a country? _____

   d. What was the year 1 hundred years ago? _____

   e. What was the year 2 hundred years ago? _____

   f. Around what year was the first airplane made? _____

   g. How long ago did the story of Troy take place?

_____

   h. About how long ago did Jesus Christ live?

_____

   i. What was the year 1 hundred years ago? _____

12. Look at the map below.
   a. Make a **U** where the United States is.
   b. Make a **C** where Canada is.
   c. Make an **S** where South America is.
   d. Make an **M** where Mexico is.
   e. Make an **F** where San Francisco is.

13. a. Name two ways that a football team can move the ball **down**

the field. _____

   b. What is it called when the team reaches the other end of the

field? _____

   c. If a team moves the ball all the way to the other end of the

field, the team gets points. How many points? _____

14. a. How are the legs of a racehorse different from the legs of a

draft horse? _____

   b. How is the back of a racehorse different from the back of a

quarter horse? _____

15. a. Fill in the blank. Eohippus lived _____ million years ago.
   b. Name two ways that the front leg of eohippus was **different**

from the front leg of a horse that lives today. _____

_____

16. When the horse went into the open fields, it changed in three ways. Name two of those ways.

_____

17. a. What clue could tell you that somebody ate chicken?

_____

b. What clue could tell you that somebody ate coconut?

_____

18. The scales in the picture tell about kilograms. Fill in the blanks to tell how many kilograms each object weighs.

a. _____   b. _____   c. _____

19. Write a homonym for each word below.

a. four _____   **d.** road _____

b. ate _____   **e.** there _____

c. new _____

20. Name two kinds of wells. _____

21. Fill in the blanks.

a. Some scales weigh things that are heavy. These scales tell how

many _____ things weigh.

b. Some scales weigh things that are not heavy. These scales tell

how many _____ things weigh.

LESSON 126

A

Look at the maps below.

1. Find A on map 1. What ocean is that? _____

2. a. What's the name of country B? _____

    b. Name two cities in country B. _____

3. What's the name of country C? _____

4. What's the name of place D? _____

5. What's the name of country E? _____

6. a. Find F on map 2. What's the name of country F? _____
    b. What happened in country F about 3 thousand years ago?

_____

7. What's the name of country G? _____

8. a. What's the name of country H? _____

    b. Name two girls who went to country H. _____

Map 1

Map 2

B

Story items

9. **Underline** three ways that people traveled two hundred years ago.
   - by car
   - by jet
   - by horse
   - by train
   - by walking
   - by water

10. **a.** About how long would it take to go from New York City to San Francisco on a good horse? _____

    b. How long does that trip take on a jet? _____

11. **a.** How fast can an ocean liner go? _____

    b. About how long would it take to go from San Francisco to Japan on a sailing ship? _____

    c. About how long does that trip take on an ocean liner? _____

12. **a.** How fast can a sailing ship go when a good wind is blowing?
    _____

    b. About how long would it take to go from New York City to Italy on a sailing ship? _____

    c. About how long does that trip take on a jet? _____

Review items

13. What is hang-time? _____

_____

14. Name two kinds of wells. _____

15. Finish the sentence. Gasoline comes from a liquid called _____

16. a. People who lived 80 thousand years ago did not have many things that we have today. Name four things they did not have.

_____

b. People who lived 80 thousand years ago did not have houses like we have.
Finish the sentence. Some of those people lived in _____

17. Look at the picture below.
   a. Make an **S** on the shadow of the dog.
   b. Make a **W** on the shadow of the house.
   c. Make an **N** on the shadow of the car.
   d. Make an **E** on the shadow of the tree.

18. Look at the picture below.

    a. What is the name of the vehicle in the picture? _____

    b. How many wheels does the vehicle have? _____

    c. What is pulling the vehicle? _____

    d. What is soldier E doing? _____

    e. What is soldier Y doing? _____

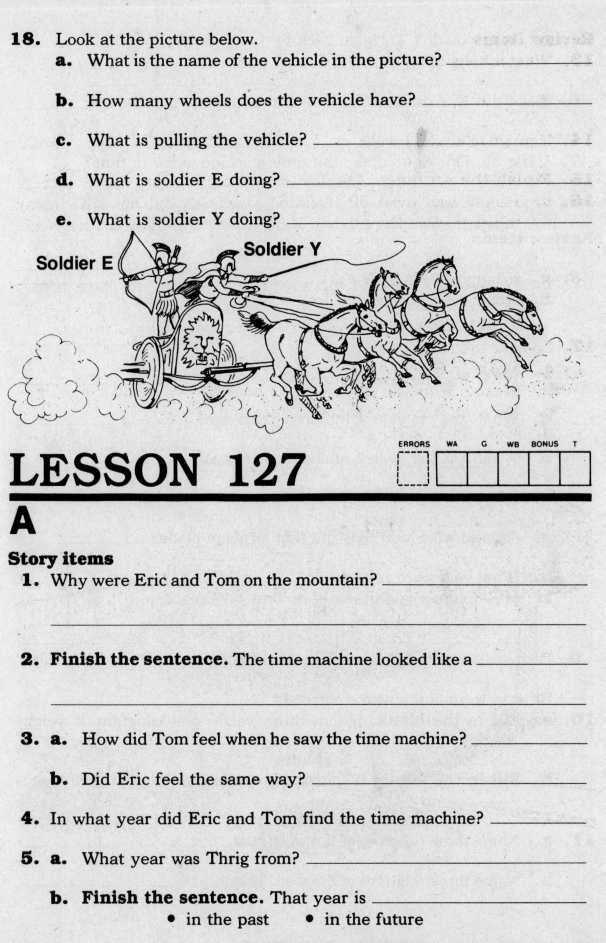

Soldier E   Soldier Y

LESSON 127

ERRORS	WA	G	WB	BONUS	T

A

Story items

1. Why were Eric and Tom on the mountain? _____

_____

2. Finish the sentence. The time machine looked like a _____

_____

3. a. How did Tom feel when he saw the time machine? _____

    b. Did Eric feel the same way? _____

4. In what year did Eric and Tom find the time machine? _____

5. a. What year was Thrig from? _____

    b. Finish the sentence. That year is _____
         • in the past   • in the future

c. Why couldn't Thrig go back to that year? _____

_____

6. What did Eric do that closed the door of the time machine?

_____

7. What did Eric do to make the time machine move in time?

_____

Review items

8. a. What year is it now? _____
   b. About how long ago did Jesus Christ live?

_____

   c. What was the year 3 hundred years ago? _____

   d. What was the year 1 hundred years ago? _____

   e. What was the year 2 hundred years ago? _____

   f. In what year did the United States become a country? _____

   g. Around what year was the first airplane made? _____

   h. What year were you born in? _____
   i. How long ago did the story of Troy take place?

_____

9. Write two words that sound the same but are not spelled the same.

Be sure to spell the words correctly. _____

10. a. Fill in the blank. If something weighs one kilogram, it weighs

_____ grams.

   b. Fill in the blank. If something weighs five kilograms, it weighs

_____ grams.

11. a. Name three relatives of the word **run.** _____

   b. Name three relatives of the word **jump.** _____

12. Look at the map.
   a. Make a **U** where the United States is.
   b. Make a **C** where Canada is.
   c. Make an **R** where South America is.
   d. Make an **M** where Mexico is.
   e. Make an **F** where San Francisco is.
   f. Make an **I** where Italy is.

AFRICA

13. **Circle** three ways that people traveled two hundred years ago.
   - by horse
   - by car
   - by water
   - by walking
   - by train
   - by jet

14. **Finish the sentence.** A second is a unit of _____

15. Look at the speed of the three baseballs flying through the air.
   a. Write **knock over** next to the ball that will knock the catcher over.
   b. Make an arrow under the catcher to show which way he will fall when the ball knocks him over.
   c. Write **knock a little** next to the ball that will knock the catcher back a little.
   d. Write **nothing** next to the ball that will not knock the catcher back at all.

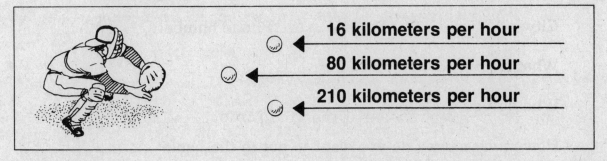

16 kilometers per hour

80 kilometers per hour

210 kilometers per hour

16. a. Which is lighter, hot air or cold air? _____

b. Look at the picture below. Which box is lighter, box A or

box B? _____

c. One box is filled with hot air. The other box is filled with cold air. Write the letter of the box that is filled

with hot air. _____

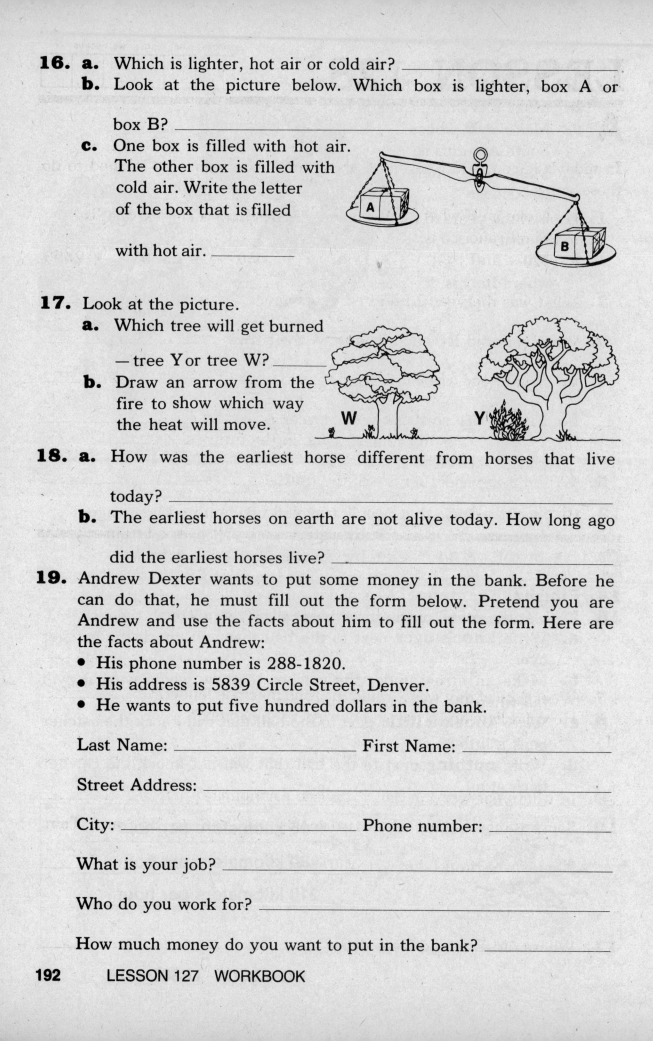

17. Look at the picture.

a. Which tree will get burned

— tree Y or tree W? _____

b. Draw an arrow from the fire to show which way the heat will move.

18. a. How was the earliest horse different from horses that live

today? _____

b. The earliest horses on earth are not alive today. How long ago

did the earliest horses live? _____

19. Andrew Dexter wants to put some money in the bank. Before he can do that, he must fill out the form below. Pretend you are Andrew and use the facts about him to fill out the form. Here are the facts about Andrew:

• His phone number is 288-1820.

• His address is 5839 Circle Street, Denver.

• He wants to put five hundred dollars in the bank.

Last Name: _____ First Name: _____

Street Address: _____

City: _____ Phone number: _____

What is your job? _____

Who do you work for? _____

How much money do you want to put in the bank? _____

LESSON 128

A

In today's lesson, you read more about time. Use what you learned to do these items.

1. Look at the years in the list below. **Underline** each year that is in the past.
   - 1920   • 1990   • 1790   • 1650   • 2380   • 2560

2. What was the year 2 hundred years ago? _____

3. What year did Eric and Tom start their trip? _____

4. a. What year was Thrig from? _____

   b. **Finish the sentence.** That year is _____
      - in the past   • in the future

5. Write three years that are in the future. _____

B

Story items

6. To what city did the time machine take Eric and Tom?

   _____

7. What time of day was it when the time machine landed? _____
8. How did Eric and Tom find out where they were?

   _____

9. In what year was the San Francisco earthquake? _____
10. Some things in San Francisco looked different to Eric and Tom.

    Name three things that were different. _____

    _____

11. Where did Eric and Tom sleep? _____

12. Finish the sentence. Most of the buildings in San Francisco were

made of _____

13. Why did fires start in the city? _____

14. What happened to Eric at the end of the story?

_____

Review items

15. List two things that show how strong an elephant is. _____

_____

16. Finish the sentence. A word that sounds the same as another

word is called a _____

17. Look at the map below.
   a. Make a **D** where Canada is.
   b. Make an **A** where South America is.
   c. Make a **T** where the United States is.
   d. Make an **X** where Mexico is.
   e. Make an **I** where San Francisco is.
   f. Make a **Y** where Italy is.

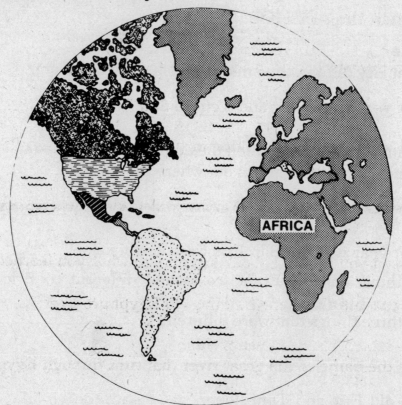

AFRICA

18. a. Name three relatives of the word **run.** _____

b. Name three relatives of the word **jump.** _____

19. a. Fill in the blank. If something weighs one kilogram, it weighs

_____ grams.

b. Fill in the blank. If something weighs six kilograms, it weighs

_____ grams.

LESSON 129

A

In today's lesson you learned more about time. Use what you learned to do these items.

1. What year did Eric and Tom start their trip? _____

2. a. What year was Thrig from? _____

b. Finish the sentence. That year is _____

• in the past   • in the future

3. In what year were Eric and Tom in San Francisco? _____

4. Around what year was the first airplane made? _____

B

In today's lesson you learned about Egypt. Use what you learned to do these items.

5. Fill in the blank. Some buildings in Egypt are over

_____ years old.

6. What is the name of the great river that runs through Egypt?

_____

7. Look at the map.
   a. Make an **I** on Italy.
   b. Make an **E** on Egypt.
   c. Make an **N** on the Nile River.

AFRICA

C

Story items

8. What year were Eric and Tom from? _____

9. Where did Eric and Tom go after leaving San Francisco? _____

10. a. Is San Francisco in the United States? _____

   b. Is Egypt in the United States? _____

11. How far back in time were Eric and Tom when they were in

Egypt? _____

12. Name the river that Tom and Eric saw when they walked out of

the time machine. _____

13. Fill in the blanks. When a _____ died, he was

buried inside a _____ with all his slaves, goats, and everything else he owned.

14. Name the two things Tom took from the time machine.

_____

15. a. Did the soldier speak English? _____

   b. Was the soldier friendly? _____

16. a. Could Tom understand the soldier? _____

   b. Why not? _____

17. If you remember the things that happened in the story, you have learned some rules about the time machine.

- One rule tells about the handle of the time machine.

   a. If you want to go back in time, which way do you move the

   handle? _____

   b. If you want to go forward in time, which way do you move the

   handle? _____

- Another rule has to do with the door of the time machine.
   c. When you sit down in the seat of the time machine, what

   happens to the door? _____

   d. When you stand up, what happens to the door? _____

Review items

18. Look at the years in the list below. **Circle** each year that is in the future.

- 1880   • 2345   • 1992   • 1967   • 2000   • 3412

19. The scales in the picture tell about grams.
Fill in the blanks to tell how many grams each object weighs.

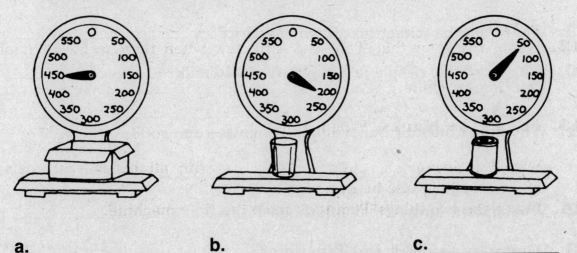

a. _____   **b.** _____   **c.** _____

LESSON 130

A

In today's lesson you read more about time. Use what you learned to do these items.

1. In what year did Eric and Tom find the time machine? _____

2. a. What year was Thrig from? _____

    b. Is that year **in the past** or **in the future?** _____

3. In what year were Eric and Tom in San Francisco? _____

4. How far back in time were Eric and Tom when they were in Egypt?

_____

5. How long ago did the story of Troy take place?

_____

6. In what year did the United States become a country? _____

B

Story items

7. What did the soldiers in Egypt think Tom was? _____

8. How did Tom try to show that he was a sun god?

_____

9. Where did the soldier take Tom and Eric? _____

10. Why didn't the people in Egypt have **cold** milk? _____

_____

11. Why didn't the king believe that Tom was a sun god?

_____

12. What did the king do to the flashlight? _____

13. What year were Eric and Tom from? _____

14. In what year was the San Francisco earthquake? _____

15. a. Is Egypt in the United States? _____

    b. Is San Francisco in the United States? _____

Review items

16. Look at the picture below. It shows a hole dug near a beach.

    a. When we dig into the pile, what's the first thing we find?

_____

    b. What's the next thing we find? _____

    c. What's the next thing we find? _____

    d. What's the next thing we find? _____

    e. What's the last thing we find? _____

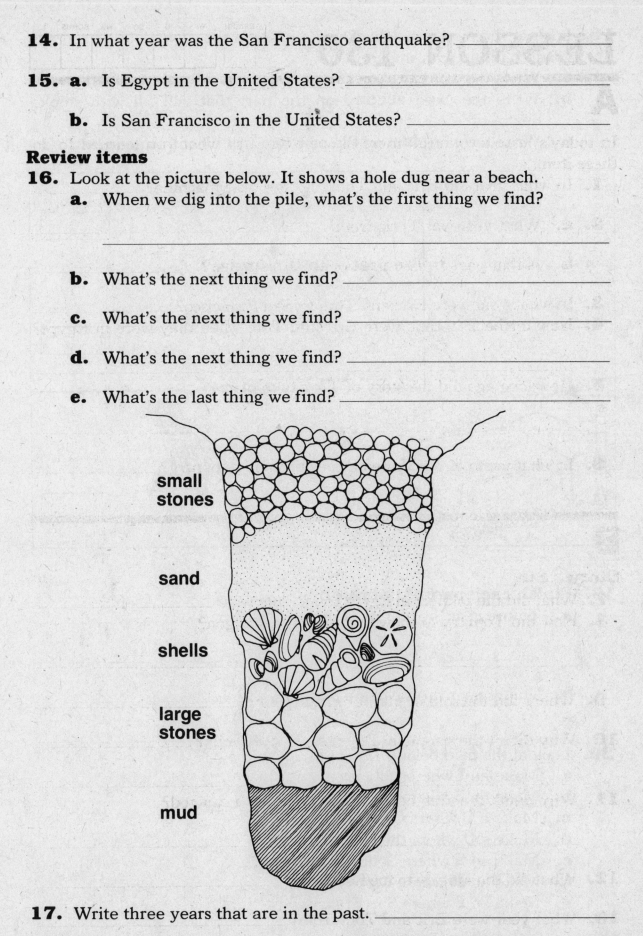

small
stones

sand

shells

large
stones

mud

17. Write three years that are in the past. _____

18. Look at the picture below. There's a fire in the room and the room is going to fill up with smoke.

a. Write the word **first** on the part that will fill with smoke first.

b. Write the word **second** on the part that will fill with smoke next.

c. Write the word **last** on the part that will fill with smoke last.

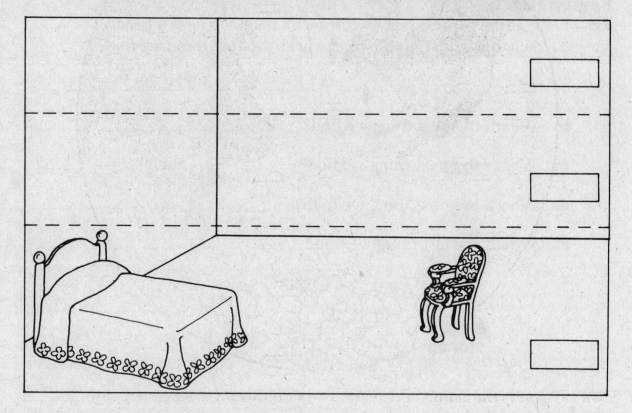

19. Finish each part of the rule.

a. Things near the bottom of the pile _____

_____

b. Things near the top of the pile _____

_____

20. Look at the map below.

a. Make an **I** where Italy is.

b. Make an **E** where Egypt is.

c. Make a **C** where Canada is.

d. Make a **U** where the United States is.

e. Make an **S** where South America is.

f. Make an **M** where Mexico is.

g. Make an **F** where San Francisco is.

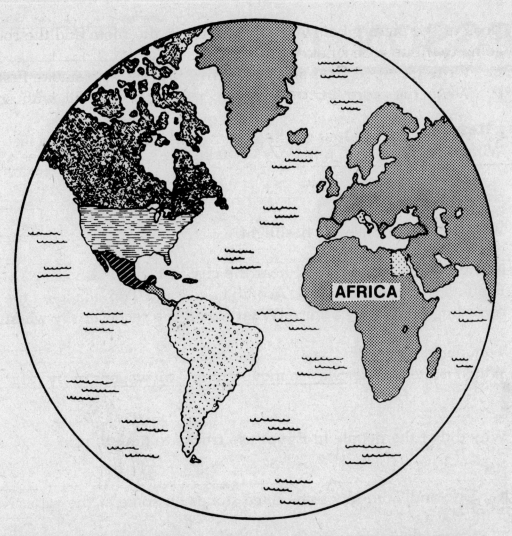

21. What is the name of the great river that runs through Egypt? _____

22. Look at the stopwatches below.

    a. How many seconds have passed on stopwatch A? _____

    b. How many seconds have passed on stopwatch B? _____

    c. How many seconds have passed on stopwatch C? _____

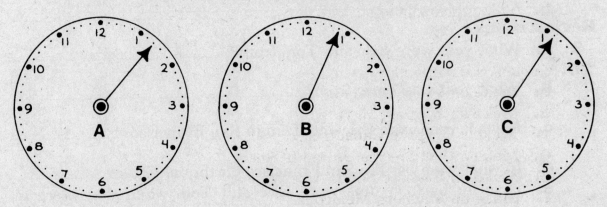

LESSON 131

A

Story items

1. What did Tom use in this story to make the king think he was a god?

   _____

2. Why didn't Tom use the flashlight? _____

3. Name the river that flowed near the city in Egypt. _____

4. Pretend that the king said, "Aso ub haki," and Tom made a tape recording of the king's voice. What would the recorder say when

   Tom played it back? _____

5. Which is the smarter way to move grain — by wagons or by raft?

   _____

6. Why didn't the people in Egypt use trucks to haul things?

   _____

7. **a.** Eric and Tom saw some huge stones on some of the rafts. Name

   three other things that were on the rafts. _____

   _____

   b. What were the stones for? _____

8. After Eric and Tom left Egypt, what walked into the time machine?

   _____

Review items

9. **a.** What year were Eric and Tom from? _____

   b. What year was Thrig from? _____

   c. In what year were Eric and Tom in San Francisco? _____

   d. In what year was the San Francisco earthquake? _____

   e. How far back in time were Eric and Tom when they were in

   Egypt? _____

10. a. How long did the war between Troy and Greece go on? _____

　　b. What did the Greek army build to help them get inside the

　　　　wall of Troy? _____

　　c. Who won the war — Troy or Greece? _____

11. The people who lived 80 thousand years ago did not live like we do.

　　a. What did the people make their clothes from? _____

　　b. What did the people use to kill animals? _____

　　c. Where did the people live? _____

　　d. Why did the people move around a lot? _____

　　_____

12. a. What is the temperature inside your body when you are

　　　　healthy? _____

　　b. **Fill in the blank.** Most fevers don't go over _____ degrees.

　　c. Name two things that may happen when people have very high

　　　　fevers. _____

　　_____

13. Look at the map.
　　a. Make an **E** where Canada is.
　　b. Make an **O** where Mexico is.
　　c. Make an **A** where
　　　　South America is.
　　d. Make a **T** where
　　　　the United States is.
　　e. Make an **R** where
　　　　San Francisco is.
　　f. Make a **J** where
　　　　Italy is.
　　g. Make a **Y** where
　　　　Egypt is.

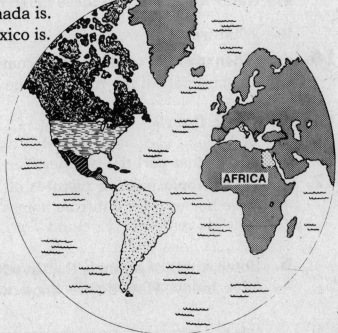

AFRICA

14. Look at the picture below. Write these names in the blanks to show where each liquid is: **crude oil, fresh water, salt water.**

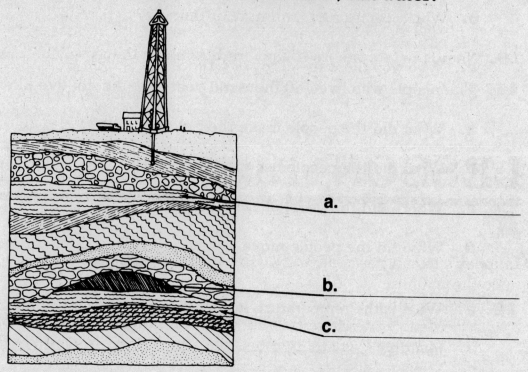

a. _____

b. _____

c. _____

15. a. Name two things that a strong magnet can pick up.

_____

b. Electricity can turn any steel bar into a magnet. What are those

magnets called? _____

c. Name a place where these magnets are used.

_____

16. a. When the air in a room becomes cooler, flies try to find the warmest part of the room. Do they sit on **the ceiling, the walls,**

or **the floor?** _____

b. Why is that part the warmest? _____

17. a. Cave people painted pictures of horses on cave walls. How are those horses different from horses that live today?

_____

b. Some kinds of animals that lived thousands of years ago are not alive today. How do we know what those animals looked like?

_____

18. a. What makes the sound of thunder? _____

    b. Which comes first, lightning or thunder? _____

19. Name the tool we use to find out how much things weigh. _____

LESSON 132

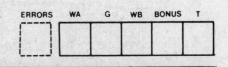

A

In today's lesson you read about Greece and Spain. Use what you learned to do these items.

  1. Look at the map below.

    a. Make an **L** where Italy is.   **d.** Make a **K** where Turkey is.

    b. Make an **I** where Egypt is.   **e.** Make an **A** where Spain is.

    c. Make a **C** where Greece is.

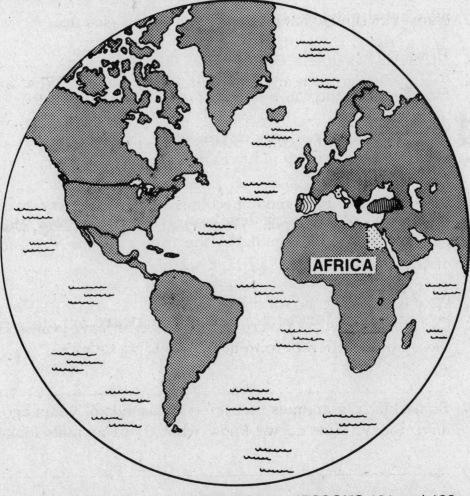

B

Story items

2. Where did the time machine take Eric and Tom after they left

Egypt? _____

3. What was the teacher in the story wearing? _____

4. Is Greece in the United States? _____
5. How far back in time were Eric and Tom when they were in Greece?

_____

6. Why did the teacher want the students to argue?

_____

7. a. Tom told Eric about a city in Greece that lost its queen. What was

the name of the queen? _____

b. To what city did the queen go? _____

8. a. How long ago did the story of Troy take place? _____

b. How long did the war between Troy and Greece last? _____

c. Who won the war — Troy or Greece? _____
d. What did that army build to help them win the war?

_____

9. a. At the end of the story, Eric and Tom left Greece. Which way
did they move the handle in the time machine — up or down?

_____

b. So will they go **forward** in time or **backward** in time? _____

Review items

10. The people who lived 80 thousand years ago did not live like we do.

    a. What did the people make their clothes from? _____

    b. What did the people use to kill animals? _____

    c. Where did the people live? _____

11. **a.** What year were Eric and Tom from? _____

    b. What year was Thrig from? _____

    c. In what year were Eric and Tom in San Francisco? _____

    d. In what year was the San Francisco earthquake? _____
    e. How many years back in time were Eric and Tom when they

    were in Egypt? _____

12. **a.** Cave people painted pictures of horses on cave walls. How are those horses different from horses that live today?

_____

    b. Some kinds of animals that lived thousands of years ago are not alive today. How do we know what those animals looked like?

_____

13. Underline three ways that people traveled two hundred years ago.

    • by bus • by walking • by horse • by jet • by water • by train

14. Finish the sentence. A second is a unit of _____

15. **a.** How long is a football field? _____
    b. Name two ways that a football team can move the ball down the

    field. _____

    c. What is it called when the team reaches the other end of the

    field? _____

    d. If a team moves the ball all the way to the other end of the field,

    the team gets points. How many points? _____

16. Name the strongest land animal in the world. _____

17. Look at the check below.

   a. When was the check written? _____

   b. Who should the bank pay? _____

   c. How much money should the bank pay? _____

   d. Whose money should the bank use to pay Ned Rice?

_____

March 10, 1981

Pay to _____ *Ned Rice* _____ 8 _____ **dollars**

Eight _____ **dollars**

Dick Ramm

LESSON 133

A

In today's lesson, you read more about time. Use what you learned to do these items.

   1. What year were Eric and Tom from? _____

   2. What year was Thrig from? _____

   3. In what year were Eric and Tom in San Francisco? _____

   4. How far back in time were Eric and Tom when they were in Greece?

_____

   5. How far back in time were Eric and Tom when they were in Egypt?

_____

B

Story items

6. The force on Eric and Tom was very great when they left Greece.

Tell why. _____

7. How far back in time were the boys in this story?

_____

_____

8. Name two kinds of animals the boys saw. _____

_____

9. Write two things that tell what a saber-toothed tiger looks like.

_____

10. Write two things that tell what a mammoth looks like.

_____

11. Why wouldn't the door of the time machine close?

_____

12. What scared the mammoth away? _____

13. Some humans ran toward the time machine. What were those humans

wearing? _____

14. What was Tom trying to do with the long branch?

_____

Review items

15. Here are some places where Eric and Tom have gone. Make an **X** after each place that is in the United States.

    a. San Francisco _____

    b. Egypt _____

    c. Greece _____

16. Look at the map below.
   a. Make an **I** where Italy is.
   b. Make an **S** where Spain is.
   c. Make a **C** where Canada is.
   d. Make an **E** where Egypt is.
   e. Make a **G** where Greece is.
   f. Make a **T** where Turkey is.
   g. Make an **M** where Mexico is.
   h. Make an **F** where San Francisco is.

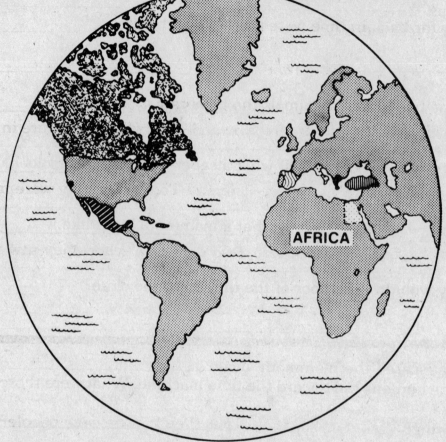

AFRICA

17. a. Let's say you are in a hot air balloon. When the air inside the balloon gets hotter, which way does the balloon move? _____

   b. Let's say you wanted to come down to the ground again. What would you do to the air? _____

18. a. What is the temperature inside your body when you are healthy? _____

   b. **Fill in the blank.** Most fevers don't go over _____ degrees.

   c. Name two things that may happen when people have very high fevers. _____

   _____

LESSON 134

A

In today's lesson you read more about time. Use what you learned to do these items.

1. What year were Eric and Tom from? _____

2. What year was Thrig from? _____

3. In what year were Eric and Tom in San Francisco? _____

4. How far back in time were Eric and Tom when they were in Greece?

   _____

5. How far back in time were Eric and Tom when they were in Egypt?

   _____

6. How far back in time were Eric and Tom when they saw the cave

   people? _____

B

Story items

7. Where did Eric and Tom go after they left the cave people?

   _____

8. About how many years in our future is the city of the future?

   _____

9. a. Could all the people in the city understand Eric and Tom? _____

   b. Why could the old man understand them? _____

   _____

10. The people in the city of the future did not fix their machines. What

    fixed their machines? _____

11. Eric and Tom couldn't get a machine that would help them work

    their time machine. Tell why. _____

12. Why did the people of the future use such simple language?

_____

13. a. After Eric and Tom left the city of the future, they saw a ship.

Was it a **modern ship** or was it an **old-time ship?** _____

b. Were Eric and Tom back in their own time? _____

Review items

14. Name two kinds of animals that lived 40 thousand years ago.

_____

15. Here are some places where Eric and Tom have gone. Make an **X** after each place that is in the United States.

a. San Francisco _____ **b.** Egypt _____ **c.** Greece _____

16. Look at the map below.

a. Make an **A** where Spain is.   **e.** Make an **E** where Mexico is.
b. Make a **B** where Canada is.   **f.** Make an **F** where South
c. Make a **C** where Egypt is.   America is.
d. Make a **D** where Greece is.   **g.** Make a **G** where San Francisco is.

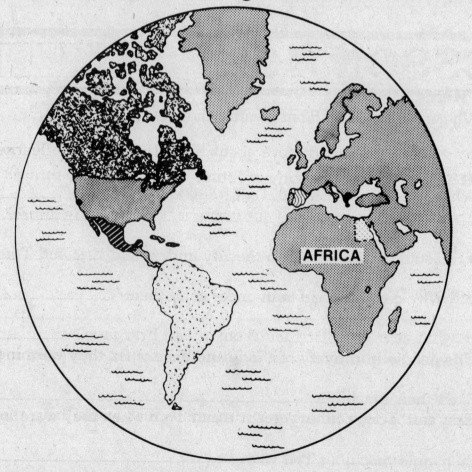

AFRICA

17. The picture shows a water wheel under the waterfall.

   a. Draw an arrow to show which way A will move.

   b. Start at B and draw a circular arrow around the shaft to show which way it will turn.

   c. Draw an arrow at C to show which way the vine will move when the shaft turns.

18. **a.** Let's say you are in a hot air balloon. When the air inside the balloon gets hotter, which way does the balloon move? _____

   b. Let's say you wanted to come down to the ground again. What would you do to the air? _____

LESSON 135

ERRORS	WA	G	CO	WB	BONUS	T

A

In today's lesson, you read more about time. Use what you learned to do these items.

   1. What year were Eric and Tom from? _____

   2. About how many years in our future is the city of the future?

   _____

   3. What year was Thrig from? _____

   4. In what year were Eric and Tom in San Francisco? _____

   5. How far back in time were Eric and Tom when they were in Greece?

   _____

   6. How far back in time were Eric and Tom when they were in Egypt?

   _____

7. How far back in time were Eric and Tom when they saw the cave

people? _____

B

In today's lesson, you read about America. Use what you learned to do this item.

8. Name four places that are in America. _____

_____

C

Story items

9. Where did Eric and Tom go after leaving the city of the future?

_____

10. a. Who discovered America? _____

    b. When did he discover America? _____

11. Is Spain in the United States? _____

12. In what year were Eric and Tom in Spain? _____

13. a. Is the world round or is it flat? _____

    b. Did Columbus think the world was **round** or **flat?** _____

    c. Did the fat man think the world was **round** or **flat?** _____

14. The fat man thought something would happen to Columbus if Columbus sailed to America. What did the fat man think

would happen? _____

_____

15. Let's say you saw a ship far out on the ocean.

    a. Would you be able to see the bottom part of the ship? _____

    b. How much of the ship would you be able to see if the world was

    flat? _____

16. What went into the time machine at the end of the story? _____

17. Why didn't the fat man like the dog? _____

_____

Review items

18. Look at the map below.
   a. Make a **P** where Spain is.
   b. Make a **C** where Canada is.
   c. Make a **U** where the United States is.
   d. Make an **E** where Egypt is.
   e. Make a **G** where Greece is.
   f. Make a **T** where Turkey is.
   g. Make an **F** where San Francisco is.

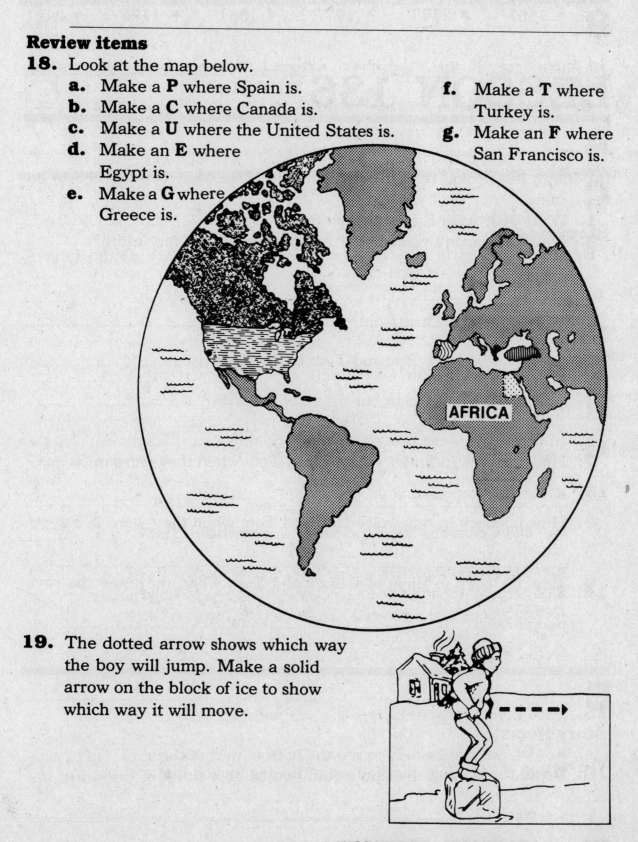

AFRICA

19. The dotted arrow shows which way the boy will jump. Make a solid arrow on the block of ice to show which way it will move.

20. What is the name of the great river that runs through Egypt? _____

21. Look at the years in the list below. **Underline** each year that is in the past.

- 1561   • 2398   • 1977   • 1881   • 1776   • 2101

LESSON 136

A

In today's lesson you read more about time. Use what you learned to do these items.

1. What year were Eric and Tom from? _____

2. About how many years in our future is the city of the future?

_____

3. What year was Thrig from? _____

4. In what year were Eric and Tom in San Francisco? _____

5. In what year did Columbus discover America? _____

6. In what year were Eric and Tom in Spain? _____

7. How far back in time were Eric and Tom when they were in Greece?

_____

8. How far back in time were Eric and Tom when they were in Egypt?

_____

9. How far back in time were Eric and Tom when they saw the cave

people? _____

B

Story items

10. Write three things that tell what the dog looked like. _____

_____

11. Who did the dog like — Eric or Tom? _____

12. Why did the fat man run away from the time machine?

_____

13. Eric wanted to take the dog with them in the time machine. Tell

why. _____

_____

14. a. Which way did Tom move the handle when they left Spain? _____

   b. Did he move the handle in the right direction? _____

   c. Did Eric and Tom go **forward** in time or **back** in time? _____

15. The boys saw a ship when the door of the time machine opened.

What kind of ship was it? _____

Review items

16. Who discovered America? _____

17. Name four places that are in America. _____

_____

18. a. Is the world **round** or **flat**? _____

   b. Did Columbus think the world was **round** or **flat**? _____

   c. Did most people in 1491 think the world was **round** or **flat**?

_____

19. Let's say you saw a ship far out on the ocean.

   a. Would you be able to see the bottom part of the ship? _____

   b. How much of the ship would you be able to see if the world was

flat? _____

20. Here are some places where Eric and Tom have gone. Make an **X**
after each place that is in the United States.

   a. San Francisco _____   **b.** Egypt _____

   c. Greece _____   **d.** Spain _____

LESSON 137

A

In today's lesson, you read about Vikings. Use what you learned to do these items.

1. Look at the map below.

  a. Make a **K** where the Land of the Vikings is.

  b. Make an **A** where Italy is.

  c. Make a **T** where Spain is.

  d. Make a **C** where Greece is.

  e. Make a **U** where Turkey is.

  f. Make a **P** where Egypt is.

  g. Make an **R** where San Francisco is.

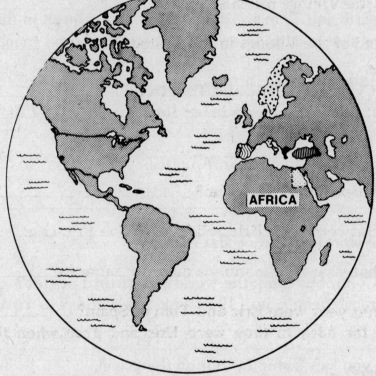

AFRICA

2. Who sailed across the ocean first, the Vikings or Columbus?

_____

3. What were the winters like where the Vikings lived?

_____

B

Story items

4. In what year were Eric and Tom in the Land of the Vikings? _____

5. Why couldn't Eric and Tom understand what the Vikings said?

_____

6. Write two things that tell what the Vikings wore.

_____

7. Why did the Vikings like Tom and Eric's dog?

_____

8. The boys were eating inside the large building. Tell why it was dark in that building.

_____

_____

9. How did the Vikings eat their meat? _____

10. Is the Land of the Vikings in the United States? _____

Review items

11. a. What year were Eric and Tom from? _____
   b. About how many years in our future is the city of the future?

_____

   c. What year was Thrig from? _____

   d. In what year were Eric and Tom in San Francisco? _____

   e. In what year did Columbus discover America? _____

   f. In what year were Eric and Tom in Spain? _____
   g. How far back in time were Eric and Tom when they were in

   Greece? _____

   h. How far back in time were Eric and Tom when they were in

   Egypt? _____
   i. How far back in time were Eric and Tom when they saw the

   cave people? _____

12. In what year did the United States become a country? _____

13. Write three years that are in the future. _____

14. Here are some places where Eric and Tom have gone. Make an **X** after each place that is in the United States.

a. San Francisco _____ **b.** Egypt _____

c. Greece _____ **d.** Spain _____

15. Look at the stopwatches below.
   a. How many seconds have passed on stopwatch A? _____

   b. How many seconds have passed on stopwatch B? _____

   c. How many seconds have passed on stopwatch C? _____

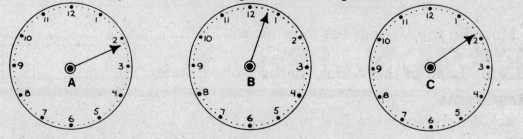

16. List two things that show how strong an elephant is. _____

_____

_____

17. Smiling Sam is tired of playing professional football. He wants to get a new job. Before Sam can do that, he must fill out the form below. Pretend you are Smiling Sam and use the facts about him to fill out the form. Here are the facts about Smiling Sam.
   • His name is Sam Green.
   • His address is 123 Cobb Street, New York City.
   • His phone number is 895-3924.
   • He wants to make one thousand dollars a month.

First Name: _____ Last Name: _____

Street Address: _____

City: _____ Phone Number: _____

What was your old job? _____

How much money do you want to make each month? _____

18. a. Which is heavier, hot air or cold air? _____

b. Look at the picture below. Which box is heavier — box M or

box S? _____

c. One box is filled with hot air. The other box is filled with cold

air. Write the letter of the box that is filled with cold air. _____

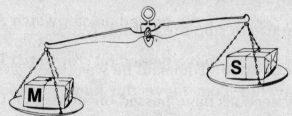

LESSON 138

ERRORS	WA	G	WB	BONUS	T

A

In today's lesson you read more about time. Use what you learned to do these items.

1. What year were Eric and Tom from? _____

2. About how many years in our future is the city of the future?

_____

3. What year was Thrig from? _____

4. In what year were Eric and Tom in San Francisco? _____

5. In what year did Columbus discover America? _____

6. In what year were Eric and Tom in Spain? _____

7. In what year were Eric and Tom in the Land of the Vikings? _____

8. How far back in time were Eric and Tom when they were in Greece?

_____

9. How far back in time were Eric and Tom when they were in Egypt?

_____

10. How far back in time were Eric and Tom when they saw the cave

people? _____

B

Story items

11. How were the Vikings from the other village different? _____

_____

12. What did Tom use to stop the fighting? _____

13. Finish the sentence. Tom said he was the god of _____

14. a. Which way did Tom move the handle when the boys left the

Land of the Vikings? _____

b. Did they go **forward** in time or **back** in time? _____

15. What season was it when the door of the time machine opened?

_____

16. What was Tom looking for when he left the time machine?

_____

17. What did Tom hear when he left the time machine? _____

18. Why couldn't Tom find his way back to the time machine?

_____

Review items

19. In what year did the United States become a country? _____

20. Look at the map.

    a. Make a **G** where the
Land of the Vikings is.

    b. Make an **I** where Italy is.

    c. Make a **P** where Spain is.

    d. Make a **T** where Greece is.

    e. Make a **C** where Egypt is.

    f. Make an **F** where
San Francisco is.

    g. Make a **U** where the
United States is.

AFRICA

21. Here are some places where Eric and Tom have gone. Make an X after each place that is in the United States.

a. Greece _____

b. San Francisco _____

c. Land of the Vikings _____

d. Egypt _____

22. Who sailed across the ocean first — the Vikings or Columbus?

_____

LESSON 139

ERRORS	WA	G	WB	BONUS	T

A

In today's lesson you read about the United States. Use what you learned to do these items.

1. The United States used to be part of another country. Name that

country. _____

2. When the United States announced that it was a country, England went to war with the United States.

a. Who was the leader of the United States army during the war?

_____

b. Which country won the war? _____

3. Who was the first president of the United States? _____

4. Who is the president of the United States today? _____

B

Story items

5. a. In what year were Eric and Tom in Concord? _____

b. In what year did the United States become a country? _____

6. Is Concord in the United States? _____

7. When Eric and Tom were in Concord, the United States was at war with another country.

a. Name that country. _____

b. Which country was winning that war in 1777? _____

8. Who helped Tom and Robert find Eric? _____

9. Tom and Eric could understand the people in Concord. Tell why.

_____

10. The English soldiers were looking for spies. What would they do to

spies that they found? _____

11. Why were the English soldiers shooting at Tom, Eric, and Robert?

_____

12. Look at the map below.
  a. Make an **A** where San Francisco is.
  b. Make a **B** where Egypt is.
  c. Make a **C** where Greece is.
  d. Make a **D** where the Land of the Vikings is.
  e. Make an **E** where Concord is.
  f. Make an **F** where Spain is.

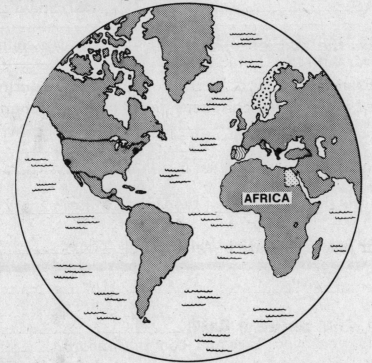

Review items
13. a. What year were Eric and Tom from? _____
  b. About how many years in our future is the city of the future?

_____

  c. What year was Thrig from? _____

  d. In what year were Eric and Tom in San Francisco? _____

e. In what year did Columbus discover America? _____

f. In what year were Eric and Tom in Spain? _____

g. In what year were Eric and Tom in the Land of the Vikings? _____

h. How far back in time were Eric and Tom when they were in

Greece? _____

i. How far back in time were Eric and Tom when they were in

Egypt? _____

j. How far back in time were Eric and Tom when they saw the

cave people? _____

14. Here are some places where Eric and Tom have gone. Make an **X** after each place that is in the United States.

a. Greece _____   **d.** Spain _____

b. Land of the Vikings _____   **e.** Egypt _____

c. San Francisco _____

15. Who sailed across the ocean first — the Vikings or Columbus?

_____

16. Name two kinds of animals that lived 40 thousand years ago.

_____

17. Name four places that are in America. _____

_____

18. a. Is the world **round** or **flat?** _____

b. Did Columbus think the world was **round** or **flat?** _____

c. Did most people in 1491 think the world was **round** or **flat?**

_____

19. Let's say you saw a ship far out on the ocean.

a. Would you be able to see the bottom part of the ship? _____

b. How much of the ship would you be able to see if the world was

flat? _____

LESSON 140

A

In today's lesson you read more about time. Use what you learned to do these items.

1. What year were Eric and Tom from? _____

2. About how many years in our future is the city of the future?

_____

3. What year was Thrig from? _____

4. In what year were Eric and Tom in San Francisco? _____

5. In what year were Eric and Tom in Concord? _____

6. In what year did the United States become a country? _____

7. In what year did Columbus discover America? _____

8. In what year were Eric and Tom in Spain? _____

9. In what year were Eric and Tom in the Land of the Vikings? _____

10. How far back in time were Eric and Tom when they were in Greece?

_____

11. How far back in time were Eric and Tom when they were in Egypt?

_____

12. How far back in time were Eric and Tom when they saw the cave

people? _____

B

Story items

13. How did Eric, Tom, and Robert find the time machine? _____

_____

14. Robert decided not to go with Eric and Tom. What was he going

to do? _____

15. The door of the time machine wouldn't close at first. Tell why.

_____

16. What was inside the door on the dashboard? _____

17. Did Tom and Eric tell the other kids where they got the dog? _____

18. What did Tom and Eric name the dog? _____

Review items

19. The United States used to be part of another country. Name that

country. _____

20. Look at the map below.

   a. Make a **V** where the Land of the Vikings is.

   b. Make an **I** where Italy is.

   c. Make a **P** where Spain is.

   d. Make a **G** where Greece is.

   e. Make a **T** where Turkey is.

   f. Make an **E** where Egypt is.

   g. Make an **F** where San Francisco is.

   h. Make a **C** where Canada is.

   i. Make a **U** where the United States is.

   j. Make an **M** where Mexico is.

   k. Make an **S** where South America is.

   1. Make an **N** where Concord is.

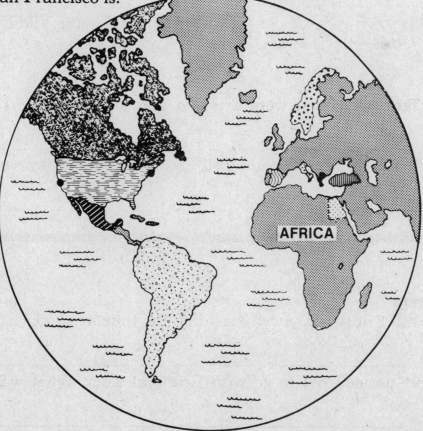

AFRICA

21. a. Who was the first president of the United States?

_____

b. Who is the president of the United States today?

_____

22. When the United States announced that it was a country, England went to war with the United States.

a. Who was the leader of the United States army during the war?

_____

b. Which country won the war? _____

23. Here are some places where Eric and Tom have gone. Mark an **X** after each place that is in the United States.

a. Concord _____ **d.** San Francisco _____

b. Land of the Vikings _____ **e.** Egypt _____

c. Greece _____

SCORECARD

1	2	3	4	5	6	7	8	9	10
11	12	13	14	15	16	17	18	19	20
21	22	23	24	25	26	27	28	29	30

FG	BONUS	TOTAL

Fact game 8
(after lesson 80)

2. Tell how many legs each animal has.
   - **a.** fly
   - **d.** mosquito
   - **b.** flea
   - **e.** cow
   - **c.** spider

3. **a.** Where is a mosquito born?
   b. What is it called when it is born?
   c. What does it have to do before it can lay eggs?

4. **a.** Which letter shows where it would be easier to walk?
   b. Why is it easier there?

5. Which arrow shows how the vine will move?

6. **a.** When you are healthy, your temperature is _____ degrees.
   b. Most fevers don't go over _____ degrees.

7. As you touch each container, tell if it holds **one liter** or **four liters.**

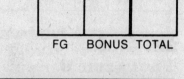

8. Tell how many grams each thing weighs.
   - **a.** Something that weighs one kilogram
   - **b.** Something that weighs six kilograms
   - **c.** A liter of fresh water

9. When things rub together, _____ .

10. Tell which nail is **hottest, next-hottest,** and **coldest.**

11. Which has more force, a waterfall that drops 30 liters every second or a waterfall that drops 10 liters every second?

12. As you touch each letter, name the object.

1	2	3	4	5	6	7	8	9	10
11	12	13	14	15	16	17	18	19	20
21	22	23	24	25	26	27	28	29	30

FG	BONUS	TOTAL

Fact game 9
(after lesson 90)

2. Gasoline comes from a liquid called _____ .

3. **a.** How long did Troy war with Greece?
   b. What did the Greek army build?
   c. Who won?

4. As you touch each letter, tell if it shows the **crude oil,** the **pipeline,** or the **refinery.**

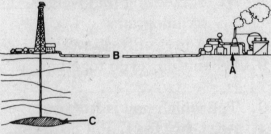

5. Which letter shows
   a. now?
   b. 1 thousand years ago?
   c. 4 thousand years ago?
   d. 2 hundred years ago?

A ●
B ● 1 hundred years ago
C ●

D ●

E ●

F ●

6. Which letter shows
   a. Troy? **b.** Greece?

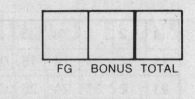

7. Tell the year
   a. the first airplane was made.
   b. 1 hundred years ago.
   c. 2 hundred years ago.

8. Tell when
   a. the United States became a country.
   b. Jesus Christ lived.
   c. Troy went to war.

9. Tell the two words that make up
   a. can't. **c.** you've.
   b. I'll.   **d.** we're.

10. As you touch each letter, tell if it shows **crude oil, salt water,** or **fresh water.**

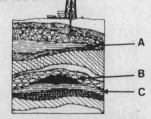

11. Name two kinds of wells.
12. Why didn't the people in Troy have telephones?

1	2	3	4	5	6	7	8	9	10
11	12	13	14	15	16	17	18	19	20
21	22	23	24	25	26	27	28	29	30

FG	BONUS	TOTAL

Fact game 10
(after lesson 100)

2. **a.** Name this vehicle.
   b. How many wheels does it have?
   c. What pulls it?

3. Which letter shows when people started cooking food?

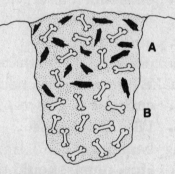

4. Spell a homonym for
   a. new.
   b. four.
   c. here.

5. What tool shows how much things weigh?

6. Tell if we use **grams** or **kilograms** for weighing
   a. heavy things.
   b. things that are not very heavy.

7. As you touch each scale, tell how many **grams** each object weighs.

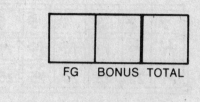

A   B   C

8. Which thing went into this pile **earlier**?
   a. W or B
   b. F or H

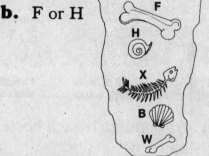

9. Which thing went into this pile **later**?
   a. W or X   **b.** H or B

10. When we dig into the pile,
    a. what's the first thing we find?
    b. what's the next thing we find?
    c. what's the last thing we find?

11. What clue could tell you that somebody
    a. ate chicken?
    b. ate coconut?

12. 80 thousand years ago, some people lived in _____ instead of houses.

SCORECARD

1	2	3	4	5	6	7	8	9	10
11	12	13	14	15	16	17	18	19	20
21	22	23	24	25	26	27	28	29	30

FG	BONUS	TOTAL

Fact game 11
(after lesson 110)

2. Name two ways horses changed when they went into the open fields.

3. **a.** What makes the sound of thunder?

   b. Which comes first — lightning or thunder?

4. As you touch each horse skeleton, tell how big it is.

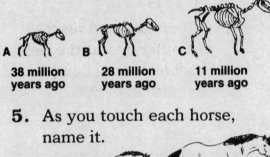

A 38 million years ago

B 28 million years ago

C 11 million years ago

5. As you touch each horse, name it.

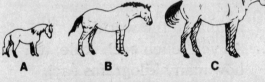

A   B   C

6. **a.** Things near the bottom of the pile _____.

   b. Things near the top of the pile _____.

7. Tell which box of air

   a. is heavier.

   b. is filled with hot air.

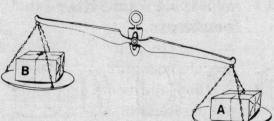

8. **a.** Which way does hot air move?

   b. Which way does cold air move?

9. Tell which letter will be in smoke **first, next,** and **last.**

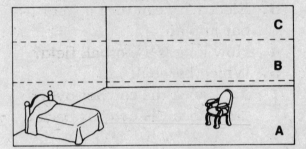

C

B

A

10. **a.** Tell when eohippus lived.

    b. Tell how big it was.

11. Tell how many third-graders weigh as much as a

    a. draft horse.

    b. quarter horse.

    c. pony.

12. **a.** When was this check written?

    b. Who should the bank pay?

    c. How much should the bank pay?

    d. Whose money should the bank use?

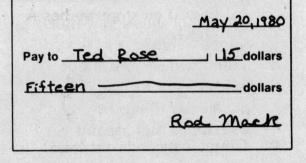

May 20, 1980

Pay to Ted Rose   15 dollars

Fifteen _____ dollars

Rod Mack

SCORECARD

1	2	3	4	5	6	7	8	9	10
11	12	13	14	15	16	17	18	19	20
21	22	23	24	25	26	27	28	29	30

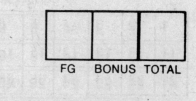

FG   BONUS   TOTAL

Fact game 12
(after lesson 120)

2. **a.** Things near the bottom of the pile _____.

    b. Things near the top of the pile _____.

3. Electricity can turn a steel bar into an _____.

4. How long is a football field?

5. Which baseball will

    a. knock the catcher over?

    b. knock the catcher back a little?

    c. not knock the catcher back at all?

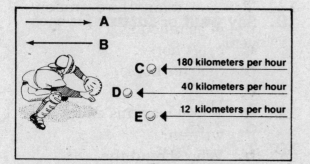

6. Which arrow shows how the catcher will fall?

7. **a.** A second is a unit of _____.

    b. Tell how much time has passed on stopwatches A and B.

    c. Count 7 seconds out loud.

8. **a.** Tell how much time has passed on stopwatches C and D.

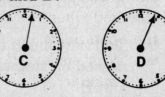

    b. Count 4 seconds out loud.

9. **a.** A football team can move the ball down the field by _____ or by _____.

    b. When the team reaches the other end of the field, it scores a _____, and the team gets _____ points.

10. Name the strongest land animal in the world.

11. As you touch each scale, tell how many kilograms each thing weighs.

12. As you touch each container, tell if it holds **one liter** or **four liters.**

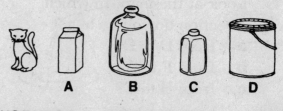

    A   B   C   D

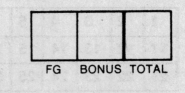

1	2	3	4	5	6	7	8	9	10
11	12	13	14	15	16	17	18	19	20
21	22	23	24	25	26	27	28	29	30

FG BONUS TOTAL

Fact game 13
(after lesson 130)

2. **a.** A second is a unit of

   _____.

   b. Tell how much time has passed on stopwatches A and B.

   c. Count 5 seconds out loud.

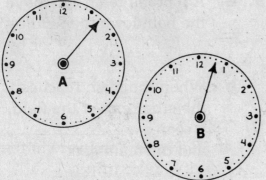

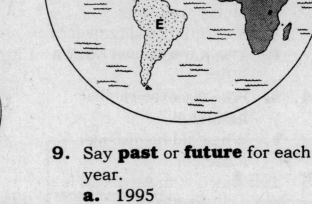

3. Name the great river that runs through Egypt.

4. Tell what year
   a. it is now.
   b. Thrig was from.

5. Tell when Eric and Tom were in
   a. San Francisco.
   b. Egypt.

6. As you touch A, B, C, and D, name each place.

7. As you touch E, F, and G, name each place.

8. Look at the map. In which direction do you go to get
   a. from D to B?
   b. from F to A?
   c. from B to C?

9. Say **past** or **future** for each year.
   a. 1995
   b. 1860
   c. 1947
   d. 2125

10. Tell the year
    a. the San Francisco earthquake took place.
    b. the first airplane was made.
    c. the United States became a country.

11. Name three ways that people traveled 2 hundred years ago.

12. Tell if we use **grams** or **kilograms** for weighing
    a. things that are not very heavy.
    b. heavy things.

1	2	3	4	5	6	7	8	9	10
11	12	13	14	15	16	17	18	19	20
21	22	23	24	25	26	27	28	29	30

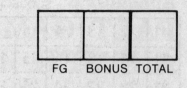

FG BONUS TOTAL

Fact game 14

(after lesson 140)

2. Name two kinds of animals that lived 40 thousand years ago.

3. **a.** When the United States became a country, it went to war with _____.

   b. The leader of the United States army was

   _____.

   c. The war was won by

   _____.

4. **a.** Who discovered America?

   b. When did he discover America?

5. Tell which of these places is in the United States:
   - Egypt • Greece
   - San Francisco

6. Tell which of these places is in the United States:
   - Concord • Spain
   - Land of the Vikings

7. As you touch A, B, and C, name each country.

8. As you touch D and E, name each place.

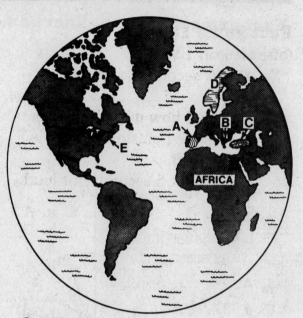

9. Tell when
   a. Eric and Tom were in the city of the future.
   b. Columbus discovered America.
   c. Eric and Tom were in Spain.

10. Tell when Eric and Tom
    a. were in Greece.
    b. saw the cave people.
    c. were in the Land of the Vikings.

11. The United States used to be part of the country of

    _____.

12. Who sailed across the ocean first — the Vikings or Columbus?

Fact game 8

2. **a.** 6
    b. 6
    c. 8
    d. 6
    e. 4

3. **a.** in water
    b. larva
    c. suck blood

4. **a.** B
    b. Because it's not as steep.

5. A

6. **a.** 37
    b. 39

7. A—1 liter
    B—1 liter
    C—4 liters
    D—4 liters

8. **a.** 1 thousand
    b. 6 thousand
    c. 1 thousand

9. they get hotter

10. hottest—B
    next-hottest—C
    coldest—A

11. a waterfall that drops 30 liters every second

12. A—tugboat
    B—dock
    C—ship

Fact game 9

2. crude oil

3. **a.** 10 years
    b. a wooden horse
    c. Greece

4. A—refinery
    B—pipeline
    C—crude oil

5. **a.** A
    b. D
    c. F
    d. C

6. **a.** C
    b. B

7. **a.** 1900
    b. *Ask your teacher for the answer.*
    c. *Ask your teacher for the answer.*

8. **a.** 1776
    b. 2 thousand years ago
    c. 3 thousand years ago

9. **a.** can not
    b. I will
    c. you have
    d. we are

10. A—salt water
    B—crude oil
    C—fresh water

11. oil, water

12. Because they weren't made yet.

Fact game 10

2. **a.** chariot
    b. 2
    c. horses

3. A

4. **a.** k-n-e-w
    b. f-o-r
    c. h-e-a-r

5. scale

6. **a.** kilograms
    b. grams

7. A—50
    B—5
    C—20

8. **a.** W
    b. H

9. **a.** X
    b. H

10. **a.** thing F; big bone
    b. thing H; shell
    c. thing W; little bone

11. **a.** chicken bones; chicken guts
    b. coconut shells

12. caves

Fact game 11

2. *Player names two:*
   They got bigger; they got faster, they ran in herds.

3. **a.** lightning
   b. lightning

4. A—about as big as a beagle
   B—about as big as a pointer
   C—about as big as a small pony

5. A—pony
   B—Mongolian horse
   C—quarter horse

6. **a.** went into the pile earlier
   b. went into the pile later

7. **a.** A
   b. B

8. **a.** up
   b. down

9. first—C
   next—B
   last—A

10. **a.** 38 million years ago
    b. about as big as a beagle

11. **a.** 30
    b. 15
    c. 4

12. **a.** May 20, 1980
    b. Ted Rose
    c. 15 dollars
    d. Rod Mack's

Fact game 12

2. **a.** went into the pile earlier
   b. went into the pile later

3. electromagnet

4. 90 meters; 1 hundred yards

5. **a.** C
   b. D
   c. E

6. B

7. **a.** time
   b. A—6 seconds
      B—8 seconds
   c. *Player counts 7 seconds.*

8. **a.** C—2 seconds
      D—4 seconds
   b. *Player counts 4 seconds.*

9. **a.** running; passing
   b. touchdown; 6

10. African elephant

11. A—40
    B—10
    C—45

12. A—1 liter
    B—4 liters
    C—1 liter
    D—4 liters

Fact game 13

2. **a.** time
   b. A—7 seconds
      B—3 seconds
   c. *Player counts 5 seconds.*

3. Nile

4. **a.** *Ask your teacher for the answer.*
   b. *Ask your teacher for the answer.*

5. **a.** 1906
   b. 5 thousand years ago

6. A—Canada
   B—United States
   C—Italy
   D—Egypt

7. E—South America
   F—Mexico
   G—San Francisco

8. **a.** west
   b. north
   c. east

9. **a.** future
   b. past
   c. past
   d. future

10. **a.** 1906
    b. 1900
    c. 1776

11. by walking, by horse, by water

12. **a.** grams
    b. kilograms

Fact game 14

2. *Player names two:*
   Horses, mammoths,
   saber-toothed tigers.

3. **a.** England
   b. Washington
   c. United States

4. **a.** Columbus
   b. 1492

5. San Francisco

6. Concord

7. A—Spain
   B—Greece
   C—Turkey

8. D—Land of the
      Vikings
   E—Concord

9. **a.** 4 thousand years
        from now; 4
        thousand years in
        the future
   b. 1492
   c. 1491

10. **a.** 3 thousand years
         ago
    b. 40 thousand
         years ago
    c. 1000

11. England

12. the Vikings